The War Chief

Edgar Rice Burroughs

The War Chief

The present edition is a reproduction of previous publication of this classic work. Minor typographical errors may have been corrected without note; however, for an authentic reading experience the spelling, punctuation, and capitalization have been retained from the original text.

ISBN: 979-8-88830-534-8

TABLE OF CONTENTS

Chapter I	Go-Yat-Thlay	1
Chapter II	Shoz-Dijiji	8
Chapter III	Yah-Ik-Tee	18
Chapter IV	The New War Chief	28
Chapter V	On the War Trail	36
Chapter VI	The Oath of Geronimo	45
Chapter VII	Raided	54
Chapter VIII	Vaqueros and Warriors	64
Chapter IX.	Love	74
Chapter X	Wichita Billings	83
Chapter XI	War Chief of the Be-Don-Ko-He	95
Chapter XII	The Scalp Dance	105
Chapter XIII	"Shoz-Dijiji Is Dead!"	114
Chapter XIV	"Fifty Apaches"	123
Chapter XV	Hunted	132
Chapter XVI	To Spirit Land	141
Chapter XVII	The Trail and Its End	148
Chapter XVIII	The War Dance	159
Chapter XIX	White and Red	167
Chapter XX	Come Back!	176

TABLE OF CONTENTS.

Chapter I.
Chapter II.
Chapter III.
Chapter IV.
Chapter V.
Chapter VI.
Chapter VII.
Chapter VIII.

Chapter IX.
Chapter X.
Chapter XI.
Chapter XII.
Chapter XIII.
Chapter XIV.
Chapter XV.
Chapter XVI.
Chapter XVII.
Chapter XVIII.
Chapter XIX.
Chapter XX.

I

GO-YAT-THLAY

NAKED but for a G-string, rough sandals, a bit of hide and a buffalo headdress, a savage warrior leaped and danced to the beating of drums. Encircling fires, woman-tended, sent up curling tongues of flame, lighting, fitfully, sweat-glistening shoulders, naked arms and legs.

Distorted shadows, grotesque, mimicking, danced with the savage and his fellows. Above them, dark and mysterious and weirdly exaggerated by the night, loomed the Grampian Hills.

Rude bows and arrows, stone-shod spears, gaudy feathers, the waving tails of animals accentuated the barbaric atmosphere that was as yet uncontaminated by the fetid breath of civilization—pardon me!—that was as yet ignorant of the refining influences of imperial conquest, trained mercenaries and abhorrent disease.

Here was freedom. Agricola was as yet unborn, the Wall of Antoninus unbuilt, Albion not even a name; but Agricola was to come, Antoninus was to build his wall; and they were to go their ways, taking with them the name of Albion, taking with them freedom; leaving England, civilization, inhibitions.

But ever in the seed of the savage is the germ of savagery that no veneer of civilization, no stultifying inhibitions seem able ever entirely to eradicate. Appearing sporadically in individuals it comes down the ages—the germ of savagery, the seed of freedom.

As the Caledonian savages danced through that long-gone night, a thousand years, perhaps, before the prototypes of Joseph Smith, John Alexander Dowie and Aimee Semple McPherson envisaged the Star of Bethlehem, a new sun looked down upon the distant land of the Athapascans and another scene—American Indian savages.

Naked but for a G-string, rough sandals, a bit of hide and a buffalo headdress, a savage warrior moved silently among the boles of great trees. At his heels, in single file, came others, and behind these squaws with papooses on their backs and younger children tagging at their heels.

They had no pack animals, other than the squaws, but they had little to pack. It was, perhaps, the genesis of that great trek toward the south. How many centuries it required no-one knows, for there

1

were no chroniclers to record or explain that long march of the Apaches from northwest Canada to Arizona and New Mexico, as there have been to trace the seed of the Caledonian savage from the Grampian Hills to the New World.

The ancestors of Jerry MacDuff had brought the savage germ with them to Georgia from Scotland in early colonial days, and it had manifested itself in Jerry in two ways—filled him with a distaste for civilization that urged him ever frontierward and mated him with the granddaughter of a Cherokee Indian, in whose veins pulsed analogous desires.

Jerry MacDuff and Annie Foley were, like nearly all other pioneers, ignorant, illiterate, unwashed. They had nothing of the majesty and grandeur and poise of their savage forebears; the repressive force of civilization had stifled everything but the bare, unlovely germ of savagery. They have little to do with this chronicle, other than to bring Andy MacDuff into the world in a dilapidated wagon somewhere in Missouri in the spring of 1863, and carry him a few months and a few hundred miles upon the sea of life.

Why Jerry MacDuff was not in one army or another, or in jail, in 1863, I do not know, for he was an able-bodied man of thirty and no coward; but the bare fact is that he was headed for California along the old Santa Fe trail. His pace was slow, since dire poverty, which had always been his lot, necessitated considerable stops at the infrequent settlements where he might earn the wherewith to continue his oft-interrupted journey.

Out of Santa Fe, New Mexico, the MacDuffs turned south along the Rio Grande toward the spot where the seeds of the ancient Caledonian and Athapascan warriors were destined to meet again for the first time, perhaps, since they had set out upon opposite trails from the birthplace of humanity in the days when ferns were trees, and unsailed seas lashed the shores of continents that are no more.

Changed are the seas, changed are the continents, changed the mortal envelope that houses the germ of humanity that alone remains unchanged and unchangeable. It abode in the breast of Go-yat-thlay, the Apache and, identical, in the breast of Andy MacDuff, the infant white.

Had Andy's forebears remained in Scotland Andy would doubtless have developed into a perfectly respectable caddie before he became a God-fearing, law-abiding farmer. Back of him were all the generations of civilization that are supposed to have exerted a refining influence upon humanity to the end that we are now inherently more godlike than our savage ancestors, or the less-favored peoples who have yet to emerge from savagery.

2

Back of Go-yat-thlay there was no civilization. Down through all the unthinkable ages from the beginning the savage germ that animated him had come untouched by any suggestion of refinement—Go-yat-thlay, born a Ned-ni Apache in No-doyohn Canyon, Arizona, in 1829, was a stark savage. Already, at thirty-four, he was war chief of the Be-don-ko-he, the tribe of his first wife, Alope, which he had joined after his marriage to her. The great Mangas Colorado, hereditary chief of the Be-don-ko-he, thought well of him, consulted him, deferred to him upon occasion; often sent him out upon the war trail in command of parties of raiders.

Today Go-yat-thlay was thus engaged. With four warriors he rode down the slopes of Stein's Peak range, dropped into a hollow and clambered again almost to the top of an eminence beyond. Here they halted and Go-yat-thlay, dismounting, handed his reins to one of his fellows. Alone he clambered noiselessly to the summit, disturbing no smallest pebble, and lying there upon his belly looked down upon a winding, dusty road below. No emotion that he may have felt was reflected in those cruel, granitic features.

For an hour he had been moving directly toward this point expecting that when he arrived he would find about what he was looking down upon now—a single wagon drawn by two mules, a dilapidated wagon, with a soiled and much-patched cover.

Go-yat-thlay had never before seen this wagon, but he had seen its dust from a great distance; he noted its volume and its rate of progress, and he had known that it was a wagon drawn by two mules, for there was less dust than an ox-drawn vehicle would have raised, since oxen do not lift their feet as high as horses or mules, and, too, its rate of progress eliminated oxen as a possible means of locomotion. That the wagon was drawn by mules rather than horses was but a shrewd guess based upon observation. The Apache knew that few horses survived thus far the long trek from the white man's country.

In the mind of Go-yat-thlay burned a recollection of the wrongs that had been heaped upon his people by the white man. In the legends of his fathers had come down the story of the conquests of the Spaniards, through Coronado and the priests, three-hundred years before. In those days the Apache had fought only to preserve the integrity of his domain from the domination of an alien race. In his heart there was not the bitter hatred that the cruelty and injustice and treachery of the more recent American invaders engendered.

These things passed through the mind of the Apache as he looked down upon the scene below; and too, there was the lure of loot. Mules have value as food, and among the meager personal

3

belongings of the white emigrants there was always ammunition and often trinkets dear to the heart of the savage.

And so there were greed and vengeance in the heart of Go-yat-thlay as he watched the wagon and Jerry MacDuff and Annie, but there was no change in the expression upon the cruel and inscrutable face.

The Indian drew himself down below the crest of the sun-scorched hill, out of sight of the unsuspecting whites, and signaled to his companions. Three of them crept upward toward him; the fourth, remaining, held the ponies of the others. He was a youth undergoing preparation for admission to the warrior class.

Go-yat-thlay spoke to the three. Separating, the four bucks crept to the hilltop. The mules plodded through the dust; their brown hides were streaked with it and by little rivulets of sweat.

Jerry MacDuff stuffed a large portion of fine cut inside his cheek and spat copiously at nothing in particular. Annie Foley re-lit her pipe. They seldom spoke. They had not spoken for many hours; they were never to speak again.

Almost before the report of the first shot reached his ears Jerry MacDuff heard a soft plop and saw Annie crumple and lurch forward. As he reached out to catch her a slug struck him in the left shoulder and he lurched to the ground on the right side of the wagon as Annie, dead now, slipped softly and silently beneath the left front wheel. The mules brought up suddenly by this unexpected obstacle, and being unurged, stopped.

When the warriors reached the scene, Jerry was trying to drag himself upward to the wagon box from whence he could reach his rifle. Go-yat-thlay struck him over the head with the butt of a Yauger and Jerry sank back into the soft dust of the road.

The sun shone down out of a blue sky; a Sabbath peace lay upon the scene; a great, white lily bloomed beside the road, mute evidence of the omnipotence of the Creator.

Jerry lay upon his back close beside the wagon. Go-yat-thlay detached a broken stake from the wagon and, with a shovel that was strapped to the side, drove it through Jerry and into the ground. Jerry groaned, but did not regain consciousness—then. For the first time the expression upon the face of the Be-don-ko-he underwent a change—he smiled.

One of his fellows called him to the opposite side of the wagon, where Annie lay, and pointed to the dead woman's sun-tanned face and straight, black hair, and the high cheek bones that her Cherokee grandsire had bequeathed her.

"Indian," he said to Go-yat-thlay.

The war chief nodded.

4

A second Indian emerged from the wagon, where he had been rummaging. He was grinning broadly. By one foot he held up for their inspection wee Andy MacDuff, whom he was about to swing heavily against the nearest iron tire when Go-yat-thlay stopped him with a gesture and holding out his hand received the descendant of one, long dead, who had been equally as savage as he. From northwestern Canada and from the Grampian Hills the seeds had met at last.

Wee Andy had seemingly inherited, through his mother, more Indian blood than flowed in her veins; at least he looked more an Indian than she, with his round face, his big, dark eyes, his straight, black hair.

Go-yat-thlay thought him an Indian; upon no other hypothesis can be explained the fact that instead of destroying him the savage chief carried him back to the hogans of his own people, notwithstanding the grumblings of Juh, who had wished to brain the spawn of the pindah lickoyee.

Thus, in the dome-shaped, thatched brush hut of Go-yat-thlay, in the arms of Sons-ee-ah-ray, his youngest squaw, ended the life history of Andy MacDuff and began that of a nameless, little Indian baby.

That night to the camp of the Be-don-ko-he and the Ned-ni came a runner from the headquarters of the Rio Mimbres. For over a hundred miles he had come on foot, across parched desert burning beneath the fiery rays of Chigo-na-ay, and over rugged mountains that no horse could travel, in sixteen hours.

Moccasins, of heavy buckskin with the toes turned up at right angles and terminating in a disc an inch and a quarter in diameter that formed a part of the rawhide sole, protected his feet and legs from the sharp stones and the cactus; a narrow head band of Apache-tanned doeskin kept his long, black hair from falling across his eyes; these and a G-string were his apparel. Some parched corn and dried meat that he had carried he had eaten on the way and he had drunk a little water from a bottle improvised from a piece of the large intestine of a horse. The only weapon that he carried was a knife.

His body glistening in the firelight, he stood before the warriors who had quickly gathered at his coming. He glanced about the circle of grim faces surrounding him. His eyes, passing over the features of Juh, Chief of the Ned-ni, and Mangas, the eighteen-year-old son of the chief of the Be-don-ko-he, stopped at last upon those of Go-yat-thlay, the Yawner.

"Bi-er-le the Cho-kon-en bring bad news to the Be-don-ko-he,"

5

he announced; "from Fort McLane he brings word that Mangas Colorado, Chief of the Be-don-ko-he, is dead."

From among the squaws and children gathered behind the warriors arose anguished wails—the wives and children of Mangas Colorado had heard.

"Tell the Be-don-ko-he how their chief died," said Go-yat-thlay.

"The hearts of the white-eyes are bad," continued Bi-er-le. "With smiles upon their lips the soldiers of the great White Father came to your camp, as you know, and invited your chief to a council.

"With four warriors he went, trusting to the honor of the pindah lickoyee, who are without honor; and when they had come to the fort, where there are many soldiers, the five were seized and thrust into a hogan with strong doors and iron bars at the windows, and at night soldiers came and killed Mangas Colorado.

"Cochise, Chief of the Cho-kon-en, heard of this and sent Bi-er-le to his friends the Be-don-ko-he, for his heart grieves with the hearts of his friends. Great was the love of Cochise for Mangas Colorado. This word, too, he sends to the Be-don-ko-he: wide is the war trail; many are the warriors of the Cho-kon-en; filled are their hearts with rage against the pindah lickoyee; if the Be-don-ko-he take the war trail for revenge the warriors of Cochise will come and help them."

A savage rumble of approval rolled round the circle of the warriors.

"Cochise takes the words of Juh from his mouth." Thus spoke the Chief of the Ned-ni. "Juh, with his warriors, will take the war trail with the Be-don-ko-he against the white-eyes."

That night the warriors of the Be-don-ko-he sat in council, and though Mangas, son of Mangas Colorado, the dead chief, was present, Go-yat-thlay was elected chief, and the next morning smoke signals rose from mountain peaks a hundred miles apart. Go-yat-thlay was calling his allies to him and Cochise, the great chief of the Chihuicahui Apaches, was answering the call; and bloody were the fights that followed as the relentless avengers, following the example of the foe, took toll of innocent and guilty alike.

But of all this wee Andy MacDuff recked naught. His big, brown eyes surveyed the world from the opening in his tsoch, in which he rode fastened securely to the back of Sons-ee-ah-ray. He gurgled and smiled and never cried, so that Morning Star and Go-yat-thlay were very proud of him and he was made much of as are all Apache babies.

Back and fourth across New Mexico and Arizona, beneath blistering sun, enduring biting cold, drenched by torrential rains, Andy jounced about upon the back of Morning Star and laughed or crowed or slept as the spirit moved him, or in camp, his tsoch suspended from the bough of a tree swayed gently with the soft evening winds.

During that year his little ears became accustomed to the cry of the coyote at night, the sudden ping of the white man's bullets, the wild war whoops of his people, the death shrieks of men, and of women, and of children; and the next year he made his first descent upon Old Mexico.

Upon that raid, in 1864, the Be-don-ko-he brought back live cattle for the first time; but it was gruelling work, caring for the wounded and keeping the cattle from straying, for the Apaches were on foot; so the following year Go-yat-thlay organized a mounted raid into Sonora; but this time the women and children were left at home. However, Wee Andy was busy learning to walk, so he did not care.

II

SHOZ-DIJIJI

THE years rolled by—happy, exciting years for the little boy, whether sitting at the feet of Morning Star listening to the legends of their people, or learning of the ways of the sun and the moon and the stars and the storms, or praying to Usen for health, for strength, for wisdom, or for protection, or being hurried to safety when enemies attacked. The chase, the battle, the wild dances, fierce oaths, loving care, savage cruelties, deep friendships, hatred, vengeance, the lust for loot, hardship—bitter, bitter hardship—a little ease; were the influences that shaped the character of the growing boy.

Go-yat-thlay told him of the deeds of his forefathers—of Maco, the grandfather of Go-yat-thlay, who had been a great warrior and hereditary chief of the Ned-ni; of Delgadito and of Mangas Colorado. He taught him how make and use the bow and the arrow and the lance, and from fierce and terrible Go-yat-thlay, who was never fierce or terrible to him, he learned that it was his duty to kill the enemies of his people—to hate them, to torture them, to kill them—and that of all the enemies of the Shis-Inday the Mexicans were the most to be hated, and next to the Mexicans, the Americans.

At eight the boy was more proficient at trailing and hunting than a white man ever becomes, nor was he any mean marksman with his primitive weapons. Already he was longing to become a warrior. Often, while Go-yat-thlay talked to him, he sat and fondled the Spencer rifle that the chief had taken from a dead soldier, his fingers itching to press the trigger as he dropped the sights upon a soldier of the white-eyes.

It was in the spring of 1873 that a boy of ten, armed with bow and arrows, moved silently up a timbered canyon along the headwaters of the Gila. He was almost naked, but for loincloth and moccasins. A strip of soft buckskin, which the loving hands of Sons-ee-ah-ray had made beautiful with colored beads, bound his brow and his straight, black hair. In a quiver of mountain lion skin he carried his arrows behind his left shoulder. He was tall for his age very straight, his skin was reddish-brown of that wondrous texture that belongs to the skin of healthy childhood; his movements were all grace, like those of a panther.

8

A mile below him, upon the rocky spur of the mountains, lay the camp of his people, the Be-don-ko-he Apaches, and with them were the Cho-kon-en and the Ned-ni. The boy played that he was a scout, sent out by the great Cochise, to spy upon the enemy. Thus always, surrounded by a world of stern realities, he in a world of make-believe that was even sterner—so is it with children.

The boy was alone in mountains filled with dangerous beasts—panthers, lions, bears; and a country filled with dangerous enemies—white men; but he was not afraid. Fear was not one of the things that he had not been taught by Morning Star or Go-yat-thlay.

The fragrance of the cedar was in his nostrils, the thin, pure mountain air filled his growing lungs and imparted to his whole being an exhilaration that was almost intoxication. If ever there was joy in life it belonged to this chief's son.

He turned a rocky shoulder that jutted across the narrow trail, and came face to face with shoz-dijiji, the black bear. Fear he had not been taught, but caution he had. He had learned that only a fool risks his life where there is nothing to be gained by the hazard. Perhaps the ancient Caledonian warriors from whose loins his seed had sprung had not learned this— who knows? At any rate the boy did not seek safety in retreat. He stopped and fitted an arrow to his bow, at the same time placing two more arrows between the second and third and third and fourth fingers of his right hand, ready for instant use. The bear had stopped in his tracks and stood eyeing the boy. He was of a mind to run away, but when the bow twanged and a piece of sharpened quartz tore into his neck where it joined his left shoulder he became suddenly a terrible engine of revengeful destruction, and voicing thunderously growl after growl, he rushed upon the boy with open jaws and snarling face. The lad knew that now it was too late to retreat and his second arrow, following close upon the first, sank even deeper into the bear's neck, and the third, just as Shoz-dijiji reared upon his hind legs to seize him, entered between the ribs under the foreleg. Then the black bear was upon him and together the two toppled from the narrow trail and rolled down among the cedars growing below. They did not roll far—fifteen feet, perhaps—when they were brought up by the bole of a tree. The boy hit with his head and lost consciousness. It was several minutes before the lad opened his eyes. Beside him lay the dead body of shoz-dijiji; the last arrow had penetrated his savage heart. The son of Go-yat-thlay sat up and a broad smile illumined his face. He rose to his feet and executed a war dance around the body of his vanquished foe, bending to the right and left, backward and forward until his body was parallel with the ground; now leaping high in air,

9

now stepping with measured tread, he circled the dead bear time and time again. Fierce shouts rose to his lips, but he held them in check for he knew that the white soldiers were searching for his people.

Suddenly he stopped dancing and looked down at shoz-dijiji, and then glanced back along the trail toward the camp that was out of sight beyond the many turns of the winding canyon. Then he stooped and tried to lift the bear; but his young muscles were not equal to the effort. Withdrawing his arrows from the bear's body and recovering his bow he clambered to the trail and set off at a brisk trot toward camp. He was sore and lame and his head ached, but what matter? Never had he been more happy.

As he entered the camp he was discovered by some playing children. "Come, son of Go-yat-thlay!" they cried. "Come and play with us!" But the son of Go-yat-thlay passed them haughtily. He went directly to where several warriors were squatting, smoking, and waited until they noticed him.

"Where is Go-yat-thlay?" he asked.

One of the warriors jerked a thumb down the canyon. "Go-yat-thlay hunts antelope in the valley," he said.

"I, the son of Go-yat-thlay," said the boy, "have killed shoz-dijiji. I, alone, shee-dah, have done this thing; but alone I cannot bring in my kill. Therefore will you, Natch-in-ilk-kisn, come and help bring in the body of shoz-dijiji, yah-tats-an?"

"You no kill shoz-dijiji, you lie," said Natch-in-ilk-kisn. "You only little ish-kay-nay."

The lad drew himself up to his full height. "The son of Go-yat-thlay, the chief, does not lie—to his friends," he added. Then he pointed to the scratches and the blood upon him. "Think you I got these playing tag with the other children?" he asked." The meat of shoz-dijiji is good. Would Natch-in-ilk-kisn rather have the wolf, the coyote and the vulture eat it than to eat it himself?"

The warrior rose. "Come, little ish-kay-nay," he said, laughing. "Natch-in-ilk-kisn joked. He will go with you."

That night was a proud night for the son of Go-yat-thlay; for at the age of ten he had killed big game and won a name for himself. Henceforth he was to be known to man as Shoz-Dijiji, and not just as ish-kay-nay—boy. He had had a name for a long time of course, but, also of course, no one ever mentioned it in his presence, since if the bad spirits ever learned his name they could, and undoubtedly would, cause him a great deal of trouble, even to sickness and death.

Go-yat-thlay was not Go-yat-thlay's name either, for he too, as all other Apaches, had a secret name that was really his though no one ever used it; and though he lived to be eighty years old and was better known all over the world than any Indian who ever lived, with the possible exception of the Sioux medicine man, Sitting Bull, yet to this day no white man knows what his name was, and few indeed were those who knew him even as Go-yat-thlay. By another name was he known, a name that the Mexicans gave him, a name that held in fear and terror a territory into which could have been dumped the former German Empire and all of Greece, and still had plenty of room to tuck away Rhode Island—Geronimo.

That night Go-yat-thlay was proud, too, for Shoz-Dijiji was all that the proudest Apache father could expect of any son; and according to the custom of the Apaches the boy was as much the son of Go-yat-thlay as though he had been the blood of his own blood.

Before the lad was sent to bed he sat at the knee of the grim chieftain and the man stroked the boy's head. "You will be a brave in no time, Shoz-Dijiji," he said. "You will be a warrior and a great one. Then you can go forth and spread terror among the pindah lickoyee, slaying them where you find them."

"You hate the white-eyes," said Shoz-Dijiji. "They are men like we; they have arms and legs, as do we, and they walk and talk. Why do they fight us? Why do we hate them?"

"Many years ago they came into our country and we treated them well," replied Go-yat-thlay. "There were bad men among them, but also there are bad men among the Apaches. Not all men are good. If we killed their bad men then they killed us. If some of our bad men killed some of them they tried to punish all of us, not seeking out just the bad men among us who had made the trouble; they killed us all, men, women and children, where they found us. They hunted us as they would wild beasts.

"They took away our lands that Usen gave us. We were told that we could not hunt where our fathers had hunted since the beginning of the world; where we had always hunted. But they hunted there, where they would. They made treaties with us and broke them. The white-eyed men do not keep their promises and they are very treacherous. I will tell you now of just a single instance that you may not forget the perfidy of the white man and that you may hate him the more. This happened many years ago, while Mangas Colorado was still living.

"Some of the chiefs of the white soldiers invited us to a council at Apache Pass. Mangas Colorado, with many others, went, believing in the good intentions of the white chiefs. Just before noon they were all invited into a tent where they were told that they would be given food, but instead they were set upon by the white soldiers. Mangas Colorado drew his knife and cut his way through

11

the side of the tent, as did several other warriors, but many were killed and captured.

"Among the Be-don-ko-hes killed then were San-za, Kia-de-ta-he, Ni-yo-ka-he and Go-pi. Remember these names and when you see a white man think of them and revenge them."

It was another day. The squaws brewed tizwin. In a group sat the warriors and the chiefs. Go-yat-thlay was still boasting about the exploit of his little Shoz-Dijiji.

"He will make a great warrior," said he to Cochise, hereditary chief of the Cho-kon-en and war chief of all the Apaches. "I knew it from the first, for when he was taken from the wagon of his people he did not cry, although Juh dragged him out by one leg and held him with his head down. He did not cry then; he has never cried since."

"He is the child of the white man," growled Juh. "He should have been killed."

"He looked like one of us, like a Shis-Inday," replied Go-yat-thlay. "Long time after I learned at the agency, when we had come back from Sonora, that his mother was a white woman."

"You know it now," said Juh.

A terrible expression crossed the cruel face of Go-yat-thlay. He leaped to his feet, whipping out his knife as he arose. "You talk much, Juh, of killing Shoz-Dijiji," he said in a low voice. "Ten times have the rains come since first you would have killed him and you are still talking about it. Now you may kill him; but first you must kill Go-yat-thlay!"

Juh stepped back, scowling. "I do not wish to kill Shoz-Dijiji," he said.

"Then keep still. You talk too much—like an old woman. You are not Naliza; when Naliza talks he says something." Go-yat-thlay slipped his knife into his belt and squatted again upon his heels. With silver tweezers he plucked the hairs from about his mouth. Cochise and Naliza laughed, but Juh sat there frowning. Juh that terrible man who was already coming to be known as "the butcher."

Shoz-Dijiji, from the interior of his father's hut, heard this talk among his elders and when Go-yat-thlay sprang to his feet and Shoz-Dijiji thought that blood would be spilled he stepped from the doorway, in his hands a mesquite bow and a quartz-tipped arrow. His straight, black hair hung to his shoulders, his brown hide was sun-tanned to a shade even deeper than many of his full-blood Apache fellows. The trained muscles of his boyish face gave no hint of what emotions surged within him as he looked straight into Juh's eyes.

"You lie, Juh," he said; "I am not a white-eyes. I am the son of

12

Go-yat-thlay. Say that I am not a white, Juh!" and he raised his arrow to a level with the warrior's breast.

"Say that he is not white or Shoz-Dijiji will kill you!"

Cochise and Naliza and Go-yat-thlay, grinning, looked at Juh and then back at Shoz-Dijiji. They saw the boy bend the bow and then Cochise interfered.

"Enough!" he said. "Go back to the women and the children, where you belong."

The boy lowered his weapon. "Cochise is chief," he said. "Shoz-Dijiji obeys his chief. But Shoz-Dijiji has spoken; some day he will be a warrior and then he will kill Juh." He turned and walked away.

"Do not again tell him that he is white," said Cochise to Juh. "Some day soon he will be a warrior and if he thinks that he is white it will make his heart like water against the enemies of our people."

Shoz-Dijiji did not return to the women and children. His heart was in no mood for play nor for any of the softer things of life. Instead he walked alone out of the camp and up a gaunt, parched canyon. He moved as noiselessly as his own shadow. His eyes, his ears, his nostrils were keenly alert, as they ever were, for Shoz-Dijiji was playing a game that he always played even when he seemed to be intent upon other things—he was hunting the white soldiers. Sometimes, with the other boys, he played that they were raiding a Mexican rancheria, but this sport afforded him no such thrill as did the stalking of the armed men who were always hunting his people.

He had seen the frightened peons huddled in their huts, or futilely running to escape the savage, painted warriors who set upon them with the fury of demons; he had seen the women and children shot, or stabbed, or led to death with the men; he had seen all—without any answering qualm of pity; but it had not thrilled him as had the skirmishes the soldiers of Mexico and the United States—ah, there was something worthy the mettle of a great warrior!

From infancy he had listened to the stories of the deeds of the warriors of his people. He had hung breathless upon the exploits of Victorio, of Mangas Colorado, of Cochise. For over three hundred years his people had been at war with the whites; their lands had been stolen, their warriors, their women and their children had been ruthlessly murdered; they had been treated with treachery; they had been betrayed by false promises.

Shoz-Dijiji had been taught to look upon the white man not only as a deadly enemy, but as a coward and a liar; even as a traitor to his fellow whites, for it was not unknown to this little Apache boy that there were many white men who made a living selling rifles and ammunition to the Indians while their own troops were in the field against them. It was no wonder Shoz-Dijiji held the whites in

13

contempt, or that to be called white was the bitterest insult that could be placed upon him.

Today, as he moved silently up the sun-scorched canyon he was thinking of these things and listening, listening, always listening. Perhaps he would hear the distant thud of iron-shod hoofs, the clank of a saber, and be the first to warn his people of the approaching enemy. He knew that there were scouts far afield— eagle-eyed men, past whom not even klij-litzogue, the yellow snake, could glide unseen; yet he loved to dream, for he was a boy.

The dreaming that Shoz-Dijiji practiced did not dull his senses; on the contrary it was thus that he made them more alert, for he lived his dreams, rehearsing always the part of the great warrior that he hoped some day to play upon the stage of life, winning the plaudits of his fellows.

And so it was that now he saw something behind a little bush a hundred feet away, although the thing had not moved or otherwise betrayed its presence. For an instant Shoz-Dijiji became a bronze statue, then very slowly he raised his mesquite bow as he strung his quartz-tipped arrow. With the twang of the string the arrow leaped to its mark and after it came Shoz-Dijiji. He had not waited to see if he had made a hit; he knew that he had, also he knew what had been hiding behind the bush and so he was not surprised nor particularly elated when he picked up Ka-Chu, the jack rabbit, with an arrow through its heart; but it was not Ka-Chu that he saw—it was the big chief of the white soldiers. Thus played Shoz-Dijiji, the Apache boy.

As he came into camp later in the afternoon he saw Cochise squatting in the shadow of his hut with several of the men of the village. There were women, too, and all were laughing and talking. It was not a council, so Shoz-Dijiji dared approach and speak to the great chief.

There was that upon the boy's mind that disturbed him—he wished it settled once and for all—yet he trembled a little as he approached this company of his elders. Like all the other boys he stood in awe of Cochise and he also dreaded the ridicule of the men and women. He came and stood silently for what seemed a long time, looking straight at Cochise until the old chieftain noticed him.

"Shoz-Dijiji is a little boy," said the lad, "and Cochise is a great chief; he is the father of his people; he is full of wisdom and true are the words that he speaks. Juh has said that Shoz-Dijiji is white. Shoz-Dijiji would rather be dead than white. The great chief can speak and say if Shoz-Dijiji be a true Apache that after this Juh may keep a still tongue in his head."

Cochise arose and placed his hand on the boy's head and looked

14

down upon him. A fierce and terrible old man was this great war chief of the Apaches; yet with his own people and more often with children was his heart soft, and, too, he was a keen judge of men and of boys.

He saw that this boy possessed in a degree equal to his own a pride of blood that would make of him a stalwart defender of his own kind, an implacable enemy of the common foe. Year by year the fighting forces of the Apache were dwindling, to lose even one for the future was a calamity. He looked up from the boy and turned his eyes upon his warriors.

"If there be any doubt," he said, "let the words of Cochise dispel it forever—Shoz-Dijiji is as true an Apache as Cochise. Let there be no more talk," and he looked directly at Juh. "I have spoken."

The muscles of Juh's cruel face gave no hint of the rage and malice surging through his savage breast, but Shoz-Dijiji, the Black Bear, was not deceived. He well knew the relentless hatred that the war chief had conceived for him since the day that Go-yat-thlay had thwarted Juh's attempt to dash out his infant brains against the tire of his murdered father's wagon, even though the lad knew nothing of the details of that first encounter and had often wondered why Juh should hate him.

As a matter of fact Juh's hatred of the boy was more or less impersonal, in so far as Shoz-Dijiji was concerned, being rather a round-a-bout resentment against Go-yat-thlay, whom he feared and of whose fame and prestige he was jealous; for Go-yat-thlay, who was one day to become world famous by his Mexican-given name, Geronimo, had long been a power in the war councils of the Apaches; further, too, the youngest and prettiest of his squaws had also been the desired of Juh. It was she who had the care of Shoz-Dijiji; it was she, Morning Star, who lavished love upon the boy. To strike at the woman who had spurned him and the man who had inflamed his envy and jealousy, Juh bided his time until he might, with impunity, wreak his passion upon the lad.

Now no one had time for thoughts of anger or revenge, for tonight was to be a great night in the camp of Cochise the war chief. For two days the bucks had eaten little or nothing in preparation for the great event; the women had brewed the tizwin; the drums were ready. Night fell. Before the entrance to his hogan stood Go-yat-thlay with his women and his children. From a beaded buckskin bag he took a pinch of hoddentin and cast it toward the moon.

"Gun-ju-le, chil-jilt; si-chi-zi, gun-ju-le; inzayu, ijanale! Be good, o Night; Twilight, be good; do not let me die!" he cried, and the women prayed: "Gun-ju-le, klego-na-ay—be good, o Moon!"

Darkness deepened. Lured by the twinkling fires of the

15

Chihuicahuis myriad stars crept from their hiding places. The purple hills turned to silver. A coyote voiced his eerie wail and was answered by the yapping pack within the camp. A drum boomed low. A naked warrior, paint-streaked—yellow, vermillion, white, blue—moved into a slow dance. Presently others joined him, moving more rapidly to the gradually increased tempo of the drums. Firelight glistened upon sweat-streaked bodies. The squaws, watching, moved restlessly, the spell of the dance was taking its hold upon them.

That night the warriors drank deep of the tizwin the women had brewed, and as little Black Bear lay in his blankets he heard the shouting, the wild laughter, the fighting and dreamed of the day when he, too, should be a warrior and be able to sit up and drink tizwin and dance and fight; but most of all he wanted to fight the white man, not his own people.

Stealing the brains of the warriors was the tizwin until their actions were guided only by stark brutish germ of savagery. Thus it came that Juh, seeing Go-yat-thlay, bethought himself of Shoz-Dijiji and his hate. Leaving the firelight and the revellers, Juh moved quietly through the outer shadows toward the hogan of Go-yat-thlay.

Black Bear lay wide awake, listening to the alluring, savage sounds that came to him through the open doorway that similarly revealed to his childish eyes occasional glimpses of the orgy. Suddenly, in the opening, the figure of a man was silhouetted against the glimmering firelight beyond. Shoz-Dijiji recognized Juh instantly and, too, the knife grasped in the war chief's sinewy hand and knew why he had come.

Beside the child lay the toys of a primitive boy—toys today, the weapons of the coming warrior tomorrow. He reached forth and seized his bow and an arrow. Juh, coming from the lesser darkness without, was standing in the doorway accustoming his eyes to the gloom of the hogan's interior.

Keen-eared savage that he was he heard no sound, for Shoz-Dijiji, too, was a savage and he made no sound—not until his bow-string twanged; but that was too late for Juh to profit by it as already a quartz-tipped shaft had torn into his right hand and his knife had slipped from nerveless fingers to the ground.

With a savage Apache oath he leaped forward, but still he could not see well in the darkness, and so it was that Black Bear slipped past him and was out of the hut before Juh could seize him. A dozen paces away the boy halted and wheeled about.

"Come out, Juh," he cried, "and Shoz-Dijiji will kill you! Come out, gut of a coyote, and Shoz-Dijiji will feed your heart to the dogs."

16

Shoz-Dijiji said other things, that are printable, but Juh did not come out, for he knew that the boy was voicing no vain boast.

An hour passed and Juh was thinking hard, for the effects of the tizwin had lessened under the stress of his predicament. Suppose the squaws should return and find him held prisoner here by a boy—he would be laughed out of camp. The thought sobered him completely.

"Juh had it not in his heart to harm Shoz-Dijiji," he said in a conciliatory tone. "He did but joke."

"Ugh!" grunted Black Bear. "Juh speaks lies."

"Let Juh come out and he will never harm Shoz-Dijiji again," dickered the chief.

"Juh has not yet harmed Shoz-Dijiji," mocked the lad in whose mind was slowly awakening a thought suggested by Juh's offer. Why not make capital of his enemy's predicament? "Shoz-Dijiji will let you go," he said, "if you will promise never to harm him again—and give him three ponies."

"Never!" cried the chief.

"The women and the children will laugh at you behind their hands when they hear of this," the boy reminded him.

For a moment Juh was silent. "It shall be as Shoz-Dijiji says," he growled presently, "so long as no one knows of this thing that has just happened, other than Juh and Shoz-Dijiji. Juh has spoken— that is all!"

"Come forth, then, Juh, and go your way," said the boy; "but remember they must be good ponies."

He stood aside as the warrior strode from the hogan, and he was careful to stand out of the man's reach and to keep his weapon in readiness, for after all he had no great confidence in the honor of Juh.

17

III

YAH-IK-TEE

ANOTHER year rolled around. Once again were the Be-don-ko-he, the Cho-kon-en and the Ned-ni camped together and with them were the Chi-hen-ne, with Victorio, old Nanay and Loco. Together they had been raiding in Chihuahua and Sonora. It had been a prosperous year for the tribes, a year rich in loot; and for little Shoz-Dijiji it had been a wonderful year. Bright, alert, he had learned much. He had won a name and that had helped him too, for the other boys looked up to him and even the great chiefs took notice of him.

Cochise had developed a real affection for the stalwart youngster, for he saw in a lad who could face fearlessly a renowned chief such as Juh was, even at that time, a potential leader of his people in the years to come.

Often the old war chief talked to Shoz-Dijiji of the exploits of his people. He told him of the many wars with the Comanches and the Navajos, of raids upon the villages of the Pimos and the Papagos; and he filled his heart with yearning to emulate the glorious deeds of the great warriors who had made terrible the name of the Apaches, the Shis-Inday, the Men of the Woods, from the Arkansas River in Colorado on the north, south to Durango, Mexico, more than five hundred miles below the border; and from the California line on the west to San Antonio, Texas, on the east—an empire as large as Europe.

"And of all this, I, Cochise, am war chief," cried the old warrior. "Soon you will be a brave. So fight that you will fill our enemies with fear and our warriors with admiration so that, perhaps, you some day may be war chief of all the Apaches."

IT was May. Flowers starred the rolling pasture land, green with grama grass on which the ponies were fattening after the gruelling months of raiding south of the border. The braves loafed much about the camp, smoking and gambling. The squaws and the children tilled a little patch of ground, and once again some of the women brewed tizwin, for there was to be a great dance before the tribes scattered to their own countries. The crushed corn had been soaked and was fermenting; the mescal was roasting upon hot stones in its pit; a Yuma squaw, a prisoner of war, was making a

18

paste of soaked maize in a metate. The paste she patted into thin, round cakes and baked.

Little Ish-kay-nay watched her, for she loved tortillas and wished to learn how to make them. Ish-kay-nay was eleven, very dirty, almost naked and entirely lovely. Her lithe young body approximated perfection as closely as may anything mortal. Her tangled hair fell over a mischievous, beautiful face from which laughing eyes, serious now, watched intently every move of the Yuma. The long, black lashes and the arched brows had not yet been plucked, for Ish-kay-nay still had three years of childhood before her. Her name means boy, and to see her romp and play was all that was necessary to make one understand why she was given that name.

Night had come. The sacrificial hoddentin had been offered to the evening and to the moon. The dancing, the feasting, the drinking commenced. Among the dancers moved the medicine men, the izze-nantan of the Apaches, tossing hoddentin, mumbling gibberish, whirling their tzi-ditindes to frighten away the evil spirits.

That night the braves got gloriously drunk. Perhaps the medicine of the izze-nantan was good medicine, for the Mexican soldiers who had come up out of the south to raid them made camp a few miles away instead of attacking that night. Had they done so the flower of the six tribes of the Apaches would have been wiped out, for even Cochise, the war chief, lay unconscious in the grip of the tizwin.

The following day the braves were tired and cross. They lay around the camp and there was much quarreling. Cochise was very sick. Go-yat-thlay, Victorio, Juh, Hash-ka-ai-la, Chief of the White Mountain Apaches, and Co-si-to, Chief of the Chi-e-a-hen, forgathered and discussed the wisdom of immediately separating the tribes before there was an open break. Well they knew the savage followers. Not for long could the tribes associate without squabbles, brawls and bloody duels. Tomorrow, at the latest, they decided, each tribe would take up its trail to its own hunting grounds.

Shoz-Dijiji, tiring of play with the other children, took his bow and arrows and his lance and started up the ridge above camp. Today he was a scout under orders from Cochise. The enemy was thought to be close and because Shoz-Dijiji had the eyes of itza-chu, the eagle, and was as brave as shoz-litzogue, the yellow bear, Cochise had sent him out alone to discover the whereabouts of the foe. Thus dreamed Shoz-Dijiji as he moved silently and swiftly up the steep mountain, taking advantage of every cover, noiseless,

19

invisible. Thus learned Shoz-Dijiji the ways of his people—the ways of the Apache.

From the headwaters of the Gila far south into the Sierra Madre mountains in Mexico, Shoz-Dijiji already knew every canyon, every peak, every vantage point. He knew where water ran or stood the year round; he knew where it stood after each rain and for how long; he knew where one might discover it by scratching in the bed of a dry stream, and where one must dig deep for its precious boon. This was but a fraction of the countless things that Shoz-Dijiji knew about his own country. He knew nothing about Latin or Greek; he had never heard of Rome or Babylon; but he could take care of himself better at eleven than the majority of white men can at their prime and he had learned more useful things from actual experience than the white boy ever learns.

Therefore, this day, though he played, he played with judgment, with intelligence. He did not just fare forth and make believe that he was scouting for an enemy—he did scout. He moved to the best position within a radius of fifty miles, and when he reached it he knew just where to look for an enemy; he knew the trails they must follow to reach his people's camp; and the first thing that he saw when he looked toward the south, toward Sonora, toward the land of their hereditary enemies, brought a wave of savage exultation surging through his brown body.

There, on the plain, twenty miles away, moving steadily toward the camp of the Shis-Inday was a long column of dust. All the six tribes lay unsuspecting below him, so it would not be Apaches that were advancing toward them, and if it were not Apaches it must be an enemy. His eyes were keen, but the column was enveloped in dust; however, he was confident from the formation that he was looking at a body of mounted troops.

For just an instant longer he watched them, while he revolved in his mind the plan of action best to follow. The enemy was ten miles south of camp, Shoz-Dijiji was ten miles north. They were mounted but it would take them longer to ascend the rocky trail than it would take Shoz-Dijiji to descend the mountain and give the warning; otherwise he would have resorted to smoke signals to apprise his people of their danger. That he might still do, but the enemy would see the signals, too, and know that the Indians were near and aware of their presence. Shoz-Dijiji pictured instead a surprise ambush in a narrow canyon just below the Apaches' camp.

Already he was leaping swiftly down the mountain side. Speed, now, meant everything and he was less careful of concealment, yet neither did he entirely neglect it, for to the Apache it was second nature. He did not fear detection by the main body of the enemy,

20

but he knew that they might have scouts far out in front, though his keen eyes had seen nothing of them. With streaming hair the boy flew down the steep declivity, as trailless as the Mountains of the Moon. If he could reach camp ten minutes ahead of the enemy his people would be saved. He knew that he could do so; there was no guess work about it.

The warriors were, for the most part, sleeping off the effects of the tizwin. Some were gambling. Others were still quarreling. The squaws, as usual, were working, caring for their babies, cooking food, preparing hides, gathering firewood; carrying water. The bosom friends, Victorio and Go-yat-thlay, were emerging from the shelter of Cochise, who was still very sick, when Shoz-Dijiji bounded into camp and ran directly to the two chiefs.

"Soldiers!" he said, and pointed down toward the plain. "From the mountain top Shoz-Dijiji saw them. There are many soldiers and they come on horses. There is yet time, if you make haste, to hide warriors on either side of the canyon before the pindah lickoyee pass through."

The chiefs asked him a few brief questions, then they ran quickly through the camp calling the warriors to arms. There was little noise, but there seemed to be a great deal of confusion. The squaws gathered up their few belongings preparatory to taking to the mountains if hard pressed. The warriors caught up their weapons and gathered around their chiefs; the Be-don-ko-he around Go-yat-thlay; the Chi-hen-ne, or Warm Springs Apaches, around Victorio; the Chi-e-a-hen to Co-si-to; the White Mountain Apaches to Hash-ka-ai-la; the Ned-ni to Juh; and the Cho-kon-en, or Chihuicahui, to Na-chi-ta, the son of Cochise.

There was hasty daubing of paint on swart faces as the chiefs led them out from camp to take the places that Go-yat-thlay, acting war chief, had allotted to each tribe. Stripped to loin cloth, moccasins and head band or kerchief the fighting men of the Apaches moved silently down among the cedars to their positions. Ahead of them Go-yat-thlay had sent scouts to ascertain the position of the enemy and before the warriors reached the place of ambush one of these had returned to say that the soldiers were but a mile from the lower mouth of the canyon.

There was ample time to dispose of his forces to the best advantage and this Geronimo did like the able war chief that he was. Swiftly, silently the savage defenders moved into position and in five minutes both sides of the canyon's rim were bristling with unseen weapons—bows, with arrows of quartz and iron, lances similarly shod, ancient Mississippi Yaugers, Spencer carbines, Springfield rifles, six-shooters from the house of Colt; filled

21

cartridge belts were strapped around slim waists, or carried across broad shoulders.

Behind the advance line there were reserves; in camp were the old men and the boys, left to guard the women and the children; though the women were often as savage fighters as their men.

From the bottom of the canyon there was no sign of all this. A soft wind soughed through the cedars and the pines; there was no other sound. Only the trees and the birds and the squirrels, it seemed, inhabited this sylvan world.

The scouts of the enemy, wary, entered the canyon. They were but a short distance in advance of the main body which consisted of a company of Mexican cavalry, well mounted, well armed, well officered; veteran Indian fighters, they were, to the last man.

Go-yat-thlay waited until that last man was well inside the jaws of death, then he raised his carbine to his shoulder and fired. It was the signal. Mingling with the staccato of the rifle fire were the war whoops of the Apaches, the commands of the officers, curses; the moans and screams of the wounded. There was no cover for the troops as the Apaches were firing down upon them from above. Terrified horses, riderless, or unmanageable from pain or fright, added to the confusion wrought by the unexpected attack. Courageous as they might be the Mexicans had no chance, and that their officers realized this at the first volley was apparent by the effort they made to extricate as large a part of their force from the trap as was humanly possible.

With six or eight troopers the commander opened fire on the hidden foe, aiming at the spurts of smoke that alone revealed the position of the Indians, and thus reduced their fire while the bulk of his command turned and raced for the mouth of the canyon, where the braves that Geronimo had placed advantageously against this very emergency fired down upon them from both sides of the rim of the canyon's lower end.

Like sheep they went to the slaughter, only a few escaping, while the handful that had remained to offer their fellows this meager chance for life were wiped out to the last man.

Shoz-Dijiji, slipping away from the camp, had sneaked to a vantage point from which he might witness the battle, and as he watched his heart filled with pride at realization of the superior generalship and strategy of his savage sire. His blood leaped to the excitement of the moment and his brown fingers itched to draw the bow against the enemy.

He saw the rout of the Mexicans and he joined the rush of yelling, whooping braves that swarmed down the sides of the canyon to dispatch the wounded and loot the dead. In his path a wounded Mexican raised himself upon one elbow and Shoz-Dijiji shot him through the throat. As the trooper sank to earth again the lad drew his hunting knife and scalped him, and his eyes blazed with the deep fire of what was almost religious exaltation as he consummated this act in the Apaches' sacred drama—war.

All about him the warriors were torturing the living and mutilating the dead and Shoz-Dijiji watched, interested; but he did not follow their examples in these things. Why he did not, he could not have told. He felt neither pity nor compassion, for he had been taught neither one nor the other by precept or example. Deep within him, perhaps, there was forming, nebulously, the conviction that in after years guided him in such matters, that it added nothing to the luster of a warrior's fame to have the blood of the defenseless upon his weapons.

He could kill with savage delight, but he took no joy in the sufferings of his victims; and in this respect he was not the only exception among his fellows to the general rule that all Apaches took delight in inflicting diabolical sufferings upon the helpless. This was not the first time that he had seen Mexican soldiers fight, and having found them fearless and worthy foes he had conceived for them that respect which every honorable fighting man feels for a brave antagonist. To have killed one, then, was a high honor and Shoz-Dijiji was filled with justifiable pride as he viewed the dripping trophy of his prowess.

Geronimo, blood-spattered, grim, terrible, saw him and smiled, and passed on to send a small party after the retreating Mexicans who had escaped, that he might be assured that there was not a larger party of the enemy to the south, or that the others did not turn back to seek revenge.

The grim aftermath of an Apache victory completed, the victorious warriors, laden with loot and bearing a few scalps, returned, exulting, boasting, to the camp, where the women and children greeted them with shrill cries of praise.

That night there was feasting and dancing—the scalp dance—and the loot was divided.

The following day four of the tribes withdrew to separate camps short distances apart, leaving only the Be-don-ko-he and the Cho-kon-en in the main camp, and there they waited until the trailers had returned and reported that the Mexicans had crossed the border in retreat; then they scattered to their own hunting grounds.

Cochise was yet very ill and so Geronimo held his tribe with the Cho-kon-en, for to him the old war chief was as a second father. He exhorted Nakay-do-klunni and Nan-ta-do-tash, the medicine men, to exert their utmost powers in behalf of the old warrior; but though

23

they made their best medicine Cochise grew weaker day by day. And then one day he called Geronimo to him where he lay in his rude shelter upon blankets and furs.

"My son," said the old chief, "the spirits of the white men that he has killed are clamoring for the life of Cochise. Nakay-do-klunni and Nan-ta-do-tash cannot make medicine strong enough to drive away the spirits of the white-eyes.

"Send then for all the great chiefs of the Apaches. Tell them to come and help Nakay-do-klunni and Nan-ta-do-tash frighten away the spirits of the pindah lickoyee, for they fear our war chiefs more than they do our izze-nantan. Go, Geronimo, or Cochise will surely die."

And so Geronimo sent runners to the four tribes, summoning Nanay and Victorio and Loco, Hash-ka-ai-la, Co-si-to and Juh; and they all came and with Geronimo and the warriors of the Be-don-ko-he and the Cho-kon-en they sat before the wigwam of Cochise and while some beat upon hides stretched over sticks they all chanted songs that would fill the spirits of the white-eyed men with fear and drive them from the body of their war chief.

They sat in a circle about a large fire beside which lay Cochise. Nakay-do-klunni and Nan-ta-do-tash, wearing the sacred izze-kloth and elaborate medicine headdress, danced in a circle about the sick man and the fire. The bodies of the izze-nantans were painted a greenish brown and upon each arm was a yellow snake with the heads toward the shoulder blades.

Upon the breast of Nakay-do-klunni was painted a yellow bear and on his back were zig-zag lines denoting lightning, while Nan-ta-do-tash had lightning upon both back and breast. Dancing, bending low to right and left, forward and back, spinning first in a circle upon the left foot and then around again in the opposite direction upon the right, they voiced a weird whistling sound. Now Nan-ta-do-tash advanced toward Cochise and sprinkled hoddentin upon his arms and legs in the form of a cross and as he backed away to resume the dancing Nakay-do-klunni took his place beside the dying chieftain and made similarly the mystic symbol upon his head and breast.

For six weeks Cochise lay ill and for nearly all of this time the warriors and medicine men, working in relays and assisted by the women and the children, sought continuously by day and by night to frighten away the malevolent spirits by incantation and by noise.

Shoz-Dijiji added his bit, for he was fond of Cochise in whom he had always found an understanding as well as a powerful friend. Genuine was the sorrow of the lad in the sickness of his friend, and

24

often he went alone into the mountains and prayed to Usen, asking him to let Cochise live; but not all the big medicine of the greatest of living izze-nantans, or even the love of a little boy could avail, and so it was that early in June, 1874, Cochise, the war chief of all the Apaches, went out upon the long, last trail.

All that night there was wailing and chanting and the beating of drums and early in the morning Geronimo and Victorio who had closed the dead chief's eyes after he had died, came and painted his face afresh as for the war trail. They dressed him in his best buckskin shirt and moccasins and wrapped him in his finest blanket, while outside the rude shelter the tribes gathered to do honor for the last time to a wise and courageous leader.

The warriors and the women were arrayed in their finest: fringed buckskin and silver and bead work; heavy earrings of turquoise and silver; necklaces of glass beads, berries and turquoise, some of them a yard long, fell, a dozen or more perhaps, over a single deep, savage chest. The chiefs and the izze-nantans wore gorgeous war bonnets or medicine headdresses and each grim face was made more terrible by the pigments of the warpath. And always there was the wailing and the sound of the es-a-da-ded.

Apart from the others sat a boy, dry-eyed and silent, sorrowing for the loss of a kindly, gentle friend. In the mind of Shoz-Dijiji, who could not recall the time when he had not known the great chief, the name of Cochise suggested naught but courage, wisdom, honor and loyalty. Shocked and angry would he have been could he have sensed the horror that that grim name aroused in the breasts of the pindah lickoyee.

Three warriors came, each leading one of Cochise's best ponies, and two stalwart braves raised the dead chieftain and lifted him astride that one which had been his favorite, in front of Chief Loco, who held the corpse in an upright position.

They bore his arms before him as they started for the grave, the procession led by four great chiefs, Geronimo, Victorio, Nanay and Juh, with the balance of his people trailing behind the two ponies that were led directly in rear of the dead chief.

Juh, glancing back, saw a lad fall into the procession directly behind the last pony and a fierce scowl made more terrible his ugly, painted face. He halted the funeral cortege and the other chiefs turned and looked at him questioningly.

"Only those of the blood of the Shis-Inday may follow a great chief to his last resting place," he announced. The others grunted acknowledgment of the truth of that statement. "Shoz-Dijiji, the son of a white-eyed man, follows the war ponies of Cochise," said Juh, angrily. "Send him away!"

The inscrutable blue eyes of Geronimo regarded the chief of the Ned-ni, but he did not speak. His hand moved to the hilt of his knife, that was all.

"Cochise himself proclaimed the boy an Apache," said Nanay. "That is enough."

"Let the boy come to the grave of his friend," said Victorio. "Cochise loved him. He is, too, as good an Apache as you or I. Did he not warn the tribes and save them from the Mexicans. With my own eyes I, Victorio, saw him slay and scalp. Let him come!"

"Let him come!" said Nanay.

"He is coming," announced Geronimo as he resumed the march toward the grave.

With a scowl Juh fell in behind the chief of the Be-don-ko-he and the procession took up again its winding way along the trail toward the burial place, the mourners chanting in wailing tones the deeds of valor of the dead chief as they bore him into the mountain fastness.

For twelve miles they marched until they came to a new-made grave, hill-hidden from the eyes of foemen. It was a large grave with its sides walled up with stone to a height of three feet. Upon its floor they laid thick blankets and upon these they laid Cochise, wrapped in his two finest; beside him they placed his weapons and his most cherished belongings; across his breast was his izze-kloth, or sacred medicine cord, and inside his buckskin shirt they tucked an amulet, a tzi-daltai, made of lightning riven wood, carved and painted by the chief himself and blessed by a great izze-nantan.

Then across the grave they laid poles of mescal, resting upon the stone walls, and over these they placed blankets to keep the dirt which they now shoveled in from falling upon the corpse. Mixed with the dirt were many stones, that the coyotes might not disturb the chief's last sleep.

During the last rites the wailing of the mourners rose and fell, merging with the drums and the chants and cries of the medicine men; and then his three ponies were led away to the northwest in the direction of the Grand Canyon three hundred miles away. At two hundred yards one of them was shot, and another a mile from the grave and the third, the favorite war pony of the dead chief, still another mile farther on, that he might be well mounted on his way to the Spirit Land.

Sorrowfully the tribes turned back toward camp, where the blood relatives of Cochise destroyed all their belongings and the tribe all its provisions, so that for forty-eight hours thereafter they were without food, for such is the custom of the Apaches.

Cochise, war chief of all the Apaches, was dead. Cochise, war chief of all the Apaches, was yah-ik-tee.

IV

THE NEW WAR CHIEF

THE council gathered, the chiefs and the warriors sitting in a great circle about a central fire. Naliza, the orator, arose and stepped within the circle.

"Men of the Shis-Inday listen to Naliza," he began. "Cochise is not present. We have many brave chiefs, but we have no war chief to whom all the tribes will listen and whom they will follow upon the war trail. It is not well that we should be thus unprepared against our enemies. Tonight we must select one who will by his bravery set our warriors an example upon the field of battle and by his wisdom lead us to victory.

"The war chief of the Be-don-ko-he has suffered great wrongs at the hands of our enemies and he has wrought upon them a great revenge. He has led his people, and often ours, many times upon the war trail against the foe. Cochise trusted him. Cochise knew that he was a great leader and upon his death bed Cochise counselled us to name Geronimo war chief of all the Apaches when Cochise should be tats-an. I, Naliza, have spoken."

Others spoke, then, some for Geronimo, some for Victorio and some for Juh, for each was a great warrior and a great chief. Then, one after another, around the great circle, each warrior cast his vote and Geronimo became war chief of all the Apaches; and later in the evening Na-chi-ta, son of Cochise, was accepted by the Cho-kon-en to succeed his father as chief of that most warlike of tribes, the Chihuicahui Apaches.

Shoz-Dijiji was squatting near the wives of the dead Cochise listening to them wail when suddenly out of the deep woods came the hoot of an owl. Instantly all was silence; the wailing ceased and the women looked at one another in terror.

"Listen!" whispered one of the squaws. "It is the spirit of Cochise, he has returned and he is trying to speak to us. What does he want?"

"Have we not done everything to make him happy on his journey to chidin-bi-kungua, the house of spirits?" demanded another.

"He is not happy, he has come back," whimpered a young

28

squaw and then with a muffled scream, she lifted a shaking finger and pointed toward the black woods. "Look! It is he, come back."

They all looked. To their overwrought imaginations, harried by days of mourning and ages of superstition, anything was possible, and it was not strange that they should see the vague and nebulous outlines of a warrior standing among the deep shadows of the trees. They shuddered and hid their faces in their blankets, and when they dared look again the apparition disappeared.

Attracted by their screams some warriors had joined them, and when they heard the cause of the women's terror they sent for Nakay-do-klunni to arrange for a feast and a dance that the spirit of Cochise might be appeased and made happy on its journey to chidin-bi-kungua.

The sorrows of death do not lie heavily or for long upon the spirit of youth and so on the morrow the children romped and played and Shoz-Dijiji organized a rabbit hunt with Gian-na-tah, his best friend, and a dozen others who could borrow or steal ponies for the purpose. Laughing and joking, they rode down to the foot of the mountains, each lad armed with a hunting club.

A mile behind them a childish figure astride a pinto pony lashed its mount with a rawhide quirt in an effort to overtake the loping ponies of the boys, and when the latter halted to discuss their plans the belated one overtook them. The first boy to discover and recognize the newcomer raised a shout of derision.

"A girl! A girl!" he cried. "Go back to camp. Only warriors follow the chase, go back to camp with the squaws and the children."

But the little girl did not go back. Her dishevelled hair flying, she rode among them.

"Go back!" shouted the boy, and struck at her pony with his hunting club.

"Go back yourself!" shrilled the little girl as she lashed him across the head and shoulders with her quirt, pushing her pony against his until he fled in dismay. The other boys screamed in derision at the discomfited one, yet some of them could not resist the temptation to bait the girl and so they rode in and struck at her pony with their clubs. Lashing to right and left her stinging quirt fell impartially upon them and their mounts, nor did she give a foot of ground before their efforts to rout her, though by the very force of their numbers it was evident that she must soon succumb in the unequal struggle.

It was then that Shoz-Dijiji rode to her side and swung his club against her tormentors, and Gian-nah-tah, following the example of his friend, took a hand in her defense.

Shoz-Dijiji, having killed a bear and scalped an enemy, stood high in the estimation of his fellows who looked upon him as a leader, so that now, when he had taken his stand upon the girl's side, the outcome of the battle was already a foregone conclusion for immediately the majority lined themselves up with Shoz-Dijiji. The vanquished scattered in all directions amid the laughter and the taunts of the victors while both sides felt gingerly of numerous bumps and abrasions. It was then that some of the boys again demanded that the girl return to camp.

She looked questioningly at Shoz-Dijiji, her great brown eyes pleading through dishevelled raven locks.

The lad turned to his fellows. "Ish-kay-nay plays like a boy, rides like a boy, fights like a boy. If Ish-kay-nay does not hunt with us today Shoz-Dijiji does not hunt. I have spoken."

Just then one of the lads cried "Ka-Chu!" and, turning, lashed his pony into a run; a jack rabbit had broken cover and was bounding away across the plain in long, easy jumps. Instantly the whole pack was after him and Ish-kay-nay was in the van. Clinging with naked knees to the bare backs of their wiry little mounts the savage children streaked after the fleeing Ka-Chu. The foremost lad, overhauling the rabbit, leaned far forward over his pony's shoulder and struck at the quarry with his hunting club. The rabbit turned directly at right angles across the pony's track and as the latter, as accustomed to the sport as the boys themselves, turned sharply in pursuit, the rider, far overbalanced following the blow he had aimed, tumbled from his mount and rolled over and over upon the turf. With wild whoops the children followed the chase and as the rabbit turned and doubled many were the spills of his pursuers. Sometimes a boy, almost within striking distance, would hurl his club at the quarry, but today Ka-Chu seemed to bear a charmed life until at last the plain was dotted with riderless ponies and unhorsed riders, and only two were left in pursuit of the rabbit. Knee to knee raced Shoz-Dijiji and Ish-kay-nay. The rabbit, running upon the boy's right was close to the pony's forefoot when Shoz-Dijiji leaned down and forward for the kill, but again Ka-Chu turned, this time diagonally across the front of the pony. Shoz-Dijiji missed, and at the same instant Ish-kay-nay's pinto stepped in a badger hole, and turning a complete somersault catapulted the girl high in air to alight directly in the path of Shoz-Dijiji's pony as it turned to follow the rabbit, and as the boy toppled from its back the active little beast leaped over Ish-kay-nay's head and galloped off with head and tail in the air.

Shoz-Dijiji rolled over twice and stopped in a sitting posture at the girl's side. They looked at each other and the girl grinned. Then

30

she reached beneath her and withdrew the flattened body of the rabbit—in falling, the girl had alighted upon the hapless Ka-Chu.

"Ish-kay-nay should have been a boy," said Shoz-Dijiji, laughing, "for already she is a mighty hunter."

Together they arose and stood there laughing. Their copper bodies, almost naked, shot back golden highlights to the sun, as the two tousled black heads bent close above the prey. The lad was already a head taller than his companion and well-muscled for his age, yet they looked more like two lads than a boy and girl, and their attitude toward one another was as that of one boy to another, and not, as yet, as of the man to the maid. Two little savages they were, blending into Nature's picture of which they were as much a part as the rolling brown plain, the tree-dotted foothills, or the frowning mountains.

Ish-kay-nay's pony, none the worse for its spill, had scrambled to its feet and trotted away a short distance, where it was now contentedly feeding upon the grama grass. Still farther away the boy's mount browsed. Shoz-Dijiji looked toward it and whistled once, shrilly. The pony raised its head and looked in the direction of the sound, then it started toward its master, slowly at first; but at the second whistle, more peremptory than the first, it broke into a gallop and came rapidly to stop before the lad.

Shoz-Dijiji mounted and drew Ish-kay-nay up behind him, but when they sought to catch the girl's pony it snorted and ran away from them. Herding it toward camp the two rode in the direction of their fellows, some of whom had regained their ponies; and, so, several of them mounted double, driving the riderless animals ahead, they came back to camp.

Thus the happy days rolled by with hunting, with games, with play; or there were long trails that led down into Sonora or Chihuahua; there were raids upon Mexican villages; upon wagon trains; upon isolated ranches; there were the enemy's attacks upon their own camps. In the springs there was the planting if the tribe chanced to be in a permanent camp and then, with wooden hoes, the children and the squaws broke the ground, planted the corn in straight rows, melons and pumpkins at haphazard about the field, and the beans among the corn.

Sometimes the children, tiring of so much work, would run away to play, staying all day and sneaking into camp at dark, nor were they ever chided by their elders; but woe betide them should one of these discover them in their hiding place, for the ridicule that was sure to follow was more bitter to the Apache taste than corporal punishment would have been.

As the boys, playing, learned to use the weapons of their people,

31

to track, to hunt, to fight, so the girls learned the simple duties of their sex—learned to prepare the maguey for each of the numerous purposes to which their people have learned to put this most useful of plants; learned to grind the mesquite bean into meal and make cakes of it; learned to dry the fruit of the Spanish bayonet; to dress and tan the hides that the braves brought in from the chase.

And together the children, under the admiring eyes of their elders, learned the gentle art of torture, practicing upon birds and animals of the wild and even upon the ponies and dogs of the tribe. Upon these activities Shoz-Dijiji looked with interest; but for some reason, which he doubtless could not have understood had he tried to analyze it, he found no pleasure in inflicting pain upon the helpless; nor did this mark him particularly as different from his fellows, as there were others who shared his indifferences to this form of sport. Apaches are human and as individuals of other human races vary in their characteristics, so Apaches vary. The Apaches were neither all good, nor all bad.

In the early summer of Shoz-Dijiji's fourteenth year Geronimo and Juh, with half a dozen other warriors, were preparing to make a raid into Mexico, and when Shoz-Dijiji heard the talk about the camp fires he determined, by hook or by crook, to accompany the war party. He told Gian-nah-tah, his best friend, of this hope which occupied his thoughts and Gian-nah-tah said that he would go too, also by hook or by crook.

"Go to Geronimo, your father," counseled Gian-nah-tah, "and tell him that Shoz-Dijiji and Gian-nah-tah wish to become warriors, and if his heart is good he will let us go out upon the war trail with him."

"Come with me, then, Gian-nah-tah," replied Shoz-Dijiji, "and I will ask him now before chigo-na-ay sets again and yan-des-tan grows dark."

Squatting beneath a tree and holding a small mirror in his left hand, Geronimo was streaking his face with vermilion, using the index finger of his right hand in lieu of a brush. He looked up as the two boys approached. There was a twinkle in his blue eyes as he nodded to them.

With few preliminaries Shoz-Dijiji went to the point. "Shoz-Dijiji and Gian-nah-tah," he said, "will soon be men. Already has Shoz-Dijiji slain the black bear in fair fight and upon the field of battle taken the scalp of the enemy he had killed. No longer do Shoz-Dijiji and Gian-nah-tah wish to remain in camp with the old men, the women and the children while the braves go upon the war trail. Shoz-Dijiji and Gian-nah-tah wish to go upon the war trail. They wish to go with the great Geronimo tomorrow. Shoz-Dijiji and

Gian-nah-tah await the answer of the great war chief of the Apaches."

Geronimo was eying them keenly while he listened in silence until the boy had finished, nor was there any change in expression to denote how he was receiving their appeal. For a while after the boy became silent the chief did not speak. He seemed to be weighing the proposition carefully in his mind. Presently he opened his lips and spoke in the quiet, low tones that were his.

"Geronimo has been watching Shoz-Dijiji and Gian-nah-tah," he said, "and is pleased with them. They are both young, but so too was Go-yat-thlay when first he went upon the war trail. The time is short. Go, therefore, this very night to the high places and pray to Usen. Make your medicine, strong medicine, in the high places. Nakay-do-klunni will bless it in the morning. Go!"

Never were two boys more elated, more enthusiastic, more imbued with a desire to shout and dance; but they did nothing of the sort. Stolidly, without a change of expression, they turned and walked away. They were Apaches and they were on the high road to becoming warriors. There are times when warriors shout and dance; but such an occasion was not one of them.

Together the two boys left the camp, heading deep into the mountains, Shoz-Dijiji leading, Gian-nah-tah stepping directly in his tracks. They did not speak, but moved silently at a dog trot, for the time was short. Better would it have been to have spent days and nights in preparation, but now this could not be. A mile from camp Gian-nah-tah turned to the left, following a branch of the main canyon up which Shoz-Dijiji continued for a matter of several miles, then, turning abruptly to the right he scaled the sloping base of the canyon wall.

Where the fallen rubble from above ended against the rocky cliff side the blackened stump of a lightning-riven pine clung precariously. Here Shoz-Dijiji paused and, searching, found a flat splinter of wood not three inches long nor an inch wide and quite thin. With a slender buckskin thong he tied the splinter securely to his G-string and commenced the ascent of the nearly perpendicular cliff that towered high above him.

Taking advantage of each crevice and projection the lad crept slowly upward. Scarcely was there an instant when a single slip would not have hurled him to death upon the tumbled rocks below, and yet he never paused in his ascent, but moved as confidently as though on level ground, up and up, until, three hundred dizzy feet above the canyon floor he drew himself to a narrow, niche-like ledge. Settling himself here with his back against the cliff and his legs dangling over the abyss, he unfastened the pine splinter from

33

his G-string and with his hunting knife set to work to fashion it to his purpose.

For an hour he worked unceasingly until the splinter, smoothed upon its two flat sides, suggested, roughly, the figure of a short legged, armless man, and had been whittled down to a length of two and a quarter inches and a width of about a sixth of its greatest dimension. Upon one flat side he carved zigzag lines—two of them running parallel and longitudinally. These represented ittindi, the lightning. Upon the opposite side he cut two crosses and these he called intchi-dijin, the black wind. When he had finished the carving he tied it firmly to a thong of buckskin which formed a loop that would pass over his head and hang about his neck.

Thus did Shoz-Dijiji, the Black Bear, fashion his tzi-daltai. From a buckskin bag upon which Morning Star had sewn pretty beads the boy took a still smaller bag containing hoddentin, a pinch of which he sprinkled upon each side of the tzi-daltai, and then he tossed a pinch out over the cliff in front of him and one over his left shoulder and one over his right and a fourth behind him.

"Be good, o, winds!" he prayed.

Another pinch of hoddentin he tossed high in air above him. "Be good, o, ittindi! Make strong the medicine of Shoz-Dijiji that it may protect him from the weapons of his enemies."

All night he stood there in the high place praying to Usen, to ittindi, to the four winds. Making big medicine was Shoz-Dijiji, the Black Bear; praying to be made strong and brave upon the war trail; praying for wisdom, for strength, for protection; praying to the kans of his people; and when morning came and the first rays of chigo-na-ay touched his eerie he still prayed. Not till then did he cease.

As deliberately as he had ascended, the Black Bear climbed down the escarpment and, apparently as fresh as when he had quit camp the preceding day, trotted rapidly down the canyon and into camp. No one paid any attention to him as he went directly to the shelter of Nakay-do-klunni, the medicine man.

The izze-nantan looked up as the youth stopped before him, and grunted.

"Nakay-do-klunni," said the lad, "Shoz-Dijiji goes upon the war trail for the first time today. All night he has prayed in the high places. Shoz-Dijiji has made strong medicine. He brings it to Nakay-do-klunni to bless, that it may be very strong." He held his tzi-daltai toward the izze-nantan.

Nakay-do-klunni, squatting in the dirt, took the amulet and blew upon it; he mumbled gibberish above it; sprinkled hoddentin upon it; made strange passes in the air that thrilled Shoz-Dijiji—Shoz-Dijiji, who could climb a sheer precipice without a thrill. Then

34

he handed it back to Shoz-Dijiji, grunted and held out his palm. The lad emptied the contents of his little pouch into his own hand and selecting a piece of duklij, the impure malachite that the whites of the Southwest call turquoise, he offered it to the izze-nantan.

Nakay-do-klunni accepted the proffered honorarium, examined it, dropped it into his own pouch and grunted.

As Shoz-Dijiji turned to depart he passed Gian-nah-tah approaching the shelter of the medicine man and the two friends passed one another as though unaware of each other's existence, for the preparation of the youth aspiring to become a warrior is a sacred rite, no detail of which may be slighted or approached with levity, and silence is one of its prime requisites.

An hour later eight warriors—grim, terrible, painted men—set out upon the war trail and with them went two hungry youths, empty since the morning of the preceding day.

V

ON THE WAR TRAIL

THROUGH rugged mountains Geronimo led his war party toward the south, avoiding beaten trails, crossing valleys only after ten pairs of eagle eyes had scanned them carefully from the hidden security of some lofty eminence. Where there might be danger of discovery he sent a scout far ahead. At night he camped upon the rocky shoulder of some mountain inaccessible to cavalry. There the novitiates brought the firewood, carried the water, if there was aught to carry, did the cooking and performed whatever labor there was to be performed.

All this they did in silence, speaking only when directly addressed by a warrior. They ate only what they were told they might eat and that was little enough, and of the poorest quality. In every conceivable way were their patience, nerve and endurance tried to the utmost, and always were they under the observation of the warriors, upon whose final report at some future council would depend their acceptance into the warrior class.

On the third day they entered Mexico, and faced a long, waterless march upon the next. That morning Shoz-Dijiji filled a section of the large intestine of a horse with water and coiled it twice over his left shoulder and beneath his right arm. Presently the water would become hot beneath the torrid rays of chigo-na-ay, and the container had been cleaned only according to Apache standards of cleanliness, yet its contents would in no way offend their palates. In quantity there was sufficient to carry them far beyond the next water hole.

Shoz-Dijiji hated to carry the water. The container sloshed about his body and ever had a tendency to slip from his shoulder. With the thermometer 118 in the shade, a hot water bag adds nothing to one's comfort, and, too, this one was heavy; but Shoz-Dijiji did not complain. He stepped lightly along the trail, nor ever lagged or sulked.

Always he watched every move that the warriors made and listened with strict attention to their few words, since the procedure and terminology of war are sacred and must be familiar to every candidate for warrior honors.

The familiar names of articles used upon the war trail were

36

never spoken, only their war names being used and the observance of every act, however trivial, was tinged with the hue of religion.

Perhaps during the long span of man's existence upon Earth there has never been produced a more warlike race than the Apaches. They existed almost solely by war and for war. Much of their country was a semiarid waste land, producing little; their agriculture was so meager as to be almost nonexistent; they owned no flocks or herds; they manufactured nothing but weapons of war and of the chase and some few articles of apparel and ornament. From birth they were reared with but one ambition, that of becoming great warriors. Their living and their possessions depended almost wholly upon the loot of war; and for three hundred years they were the scourge of a territory as large as Europe, a thickly settled portion of which they entirely depopulated.

Upon such facts as these had Shoz-Dijiji and Gian-nah-tah been raised, and now they were taking the first step toward becoming one of these mighty warriors, the very mention of whose names was sufficient to bring terror to an entire community of white men.

Sometimes when they were alone or unobserved the boys conversed, and upon one of these occasions Shoz-Dijiji exclaimed: "How wonderful to have been born an Apache! I should think that the white-eyed men would prefer death to the shame of not being Apaches. They have no great warriors or we should have heard of them and no one is afraid of them. We kill their people and they fear us so that they promise to feed us in idleness if we will kill no more. What manner of men are they who are so without shame! If other men kill our people, do we feed them and beg them to do so no more? No! we go among them and slay ten for every Apache that they have killed."

"There are many of them," sighed Gian-nah-tah. "For every ten we kill, there are a hundred more to come. Some day there will be so many that we cannot kill them all; then what will become of the Apaches?"

"You have listened to the talk of Nanay," replied Shoz-Dijiji. "He is getting old. He does not know what he is talking about. The more white-eyes there are the more we can kill. Nothing would suit Shoz-Dijiji better. I hate them and when I am a great warrior I shall kill and kill and kill."

"Yes," said Gian-nah-tah, "that will be great medicine, if it does not happen that there are more white-eyes than we can kill. If there are we are the ones who will be killed."

In the mountains of Sonora Geronimo camped where he had an almost impassable mountain fastness at his back and a view of a

37

broad valley spread out below him, and he was secure in the knowledge that no enemy could reach him undetected.

The very first day their scouts discovered a wagon train winding up the valley at their feet and Geronimo sent two braves down among the foothills to spy upon it. All day the train wound up the valley and all day savage, unseen eyes watched its every move, saw it go into camp, saw the precautions that were taken to prevent attack, and carried the word back to the war chief, who had been scouting in another direction.

"There are twenty wagons, each drawn by eight mules," the scout reported to Geronimo. "There are twenty Mexicans, well armed. They ride with their weapons beside them. It is as though they feared attack, for they are often peering this way and that, and always those in the rear keep well closed up and glance back often— there are no stragglers."

"And in camp?" inquired Geronimo.

"They form their wagons in a circle and inside the circle are the mules and the men. There were two armed men on guard. They are vigilant."

"They are men," said Geronimo. "Some time they will relax their vigilance." He turned toward the youths who were busy at the camp fire. "Shoz-Dijiji," he called, "come here!"

The lad came and stood before the war chief. "There, in the valley," said Geronimo, pointing, "the Mexicans are camped. Go and watch them. Creep as closely to them as you can. If they see you you will be killed. Return at dawn and tell Geronimo all that you have discovered. Do not alarm them and do not attack unless you are discovered. Go!"

Supperless, Shoz-Dijiji faded into the twilight. A shadow, he moved in denser shadows, keeping to the hills until he came opposite the camp fires of the freighters. It was dark; the men around the camp fire could not possibly see far out into the night; yet Shoz-Dijiji did not relax his wariness.

Stooping low, sometimes creeping upon his belly, taking advantage of whatever cover the plain offered, he advanced closer and closer to the parked wagons. While yet a considerable distance from them he silently whittled a bush from its stem, close to the ground, and when he had come within a hundred yards of the nearest wagon he was crawling forward upon his belly, holding the bush in front of him. He moved very slowly and very cautiously, advancing by inches, for the art of successful stalking is the art of infinite patience. After a short advance he would lie still for a long time.

He could hear the voices of the men gathered about the fire. He

38

could see one of the armed guards, the one nearer him. The man moved back and forth just inside the enclosure, occasionally pausing to watch and listen at the gaps between the wagons. It was when he was turned away from him that Shoz-Dijiji advanced. At last he lay within a foot of one of the wagon wheels and directly behind it.

Now he could hear much of the conversation and what he heard he understood fairly well, for his people had often traded amicably with Mexicans, posing as friendly Indians, though the next day they might be planning to massacre their hosts, and there had been Mexican prisoners in the camps of the Be-don-ko-he. Through, such contacts he had gained a smattering of Spanish, just as he was to acquire a smattering of English, above the border, within the next year or two.

He heard the guard, passing close in front of him, grumbling "This is foolish," he called to someone at the camp fire. "We have not seen an Indian or an Indian sign this whole trip. I do not believe that there is an Apache within three hundred miles of us."

A big man, with a black mustache, squatting before the fire, removed his cigarette from his mouth.

"Neither do I," he replied; "but I do not know. I am taking no chances. I told you before we came out that we would stand guard every night, turn and turn about, and as long as I am captain of this train we shall."

The other grumbled and turned to look out toward the mountains across the pole of one of the wagons. Within six feet of him lay an Apache. All night he lay there watching, listening.

He learned where they would halt during the heat of the following midday; he learned where they would camp the next night and the night following that; he saw that guards were changed every two hours and that thus the men lost but two hours sleep every other night. There was no reason, therefore, on this score, why they should be too sleepy to watch efficiently. He saw that all of the men slept with their rifles and six-shooters within easy reach. He knew that a night attack would find them ready and would have little chance for success.

Shortly before dawn the wind, which had been blowing gently up the valley, changed and blew from the hills behind Shoz-Dijiji and across the camp. Instantly the Apache noted the change and watched the mules. At the same time he commenced to worm himself away from the parked wagons, holding the bush always as a screen between himself and the camp of the enemy.

He saw a mule raise its head and sniff the air, then another and another. They moved about restlessly and many of them were

39

looking out in his direction. This he could see in the light of the fire that the sentries had kept burning all night. He retreated more rapidly for he knew that the animals had caught the scent of an Indian, and he feared that the men would interpret their restlessness correctly.

Already the nearer guard had called to his fellow and both were straining their eyes out into the night, and then, just behind him, Shoz-Dijiji heard the wail of a coyote. He saw the tense attitudes of the men relax as they turned to resume their beats, and he smiled inwardly as he realized that they attributed the restlessness of their stock to the scent of the coyote. An hour later he entered camp as silently as he had left it the previous evening.

Geronimo listened to his report, and, after the custom of the Apaches, without interruption or comment until Shoz-Dijiji indicated that he had done speaking. He gave no praise, but he asked no questions; rather the highest praise that he could have bestowed, since it indicated that the youth's report was so clear and so complete as to leave no detail of information lacking.

For two days and two nights thereafter the Apaches followed the freighters, and there was scarcely a moment during that time that the Mexicans were not under close observation as the Indians waited and watched patiently for the moment that the guard of the quarry would be momentarily lowered, the inevitable moment that the shrewd Geronimo knew would come. Keeping to the hills, along the foot of which the wagon road wound, the noiseless, invisible stalkers followed doggedly the slow moving train.

In the gory lexicon of Apache military science there appears no such word as chance. To risk one's life, to sacrifice one's warriors needlessly, is the part of a fool, not of a successful war chief. To give the other fellow a chance is the acme of asininity. In the event of battle men must be killed. If all the killed are among the enemy so much greater is the credit due the victorious chief. They have reduced the art of war to its most primitive conception; they have stripped it stark to its ultimate purpose, leaving the unlovely truth of it quite naked, unadorned by sophistries or hypocrisies—to kill without being killed.

At length Geronimo was convinced of the truth he had at first sensed—that the Mexicans were most vulnerable during their midday rest. Then their wagons were not parked into a circular fortress. The men were hot and tired and drowsy. They were lulled into a fancied security by the fact that they could see to great distances in all directions. Nothing as large as a man could approach them unseen. He had even noted that upon one occasion

40

the entire party had dozed simultaneously at a noonday stop, and he made his plans accordingly.

From his intimate knowledge of the country, the trail, and the customs of freighters he knew where the noon stop upon the third day of the trailing would be made. That forenoon only one Apache trailed the unsuspecting Mexicans; the others were far ahead.

Noon approached. The complaining wheels of the great wagons jolted over the ruts of the road. The sweating mules pulled evenly and steadily. The drivers, with their single lines and their great bull-hide whips, urged their teams only sufficiently to keep the train well closed up.

Lackadaisically, soporifically, mechanically, they flicked the leaders with their long, pliant lashes. They did not curse their mules in strident voices as would American skinners. Sometimes they talked to them in low tones, or, again, they sang, and the mules plodded on through the dust, which rose in great clouds as they crossed a low, alkali flat, from which they emerged about noon upon higher, sandy ground, where the pulling was harder, but where there was no dust.

Presently the leading wagon stopped and the others drew up about it, but in no regular formation. To their left the flat plain rose gently to meet the hills a mile away. To the right, in front of them and behind they could see to the distant mountains, empurpled by haze. A brilliant sun seared down upon the scorched land, a pitilessly revealing sun in the light of which nothing could hide. There was no breeze; nothing moved and there was no sound. Just silence was there except as it was broken by the breathing of the mules, the creaking or the jangling of a bit of harness.

The captain of the train scanned the landscape in all directions. Nothing moved, there was nothing irregular within his range of vision. Had there been he would have seen it, for he had spent the best part of his life tracking back and forth across Sonora.

"Keep a watch, Manuel," he directed one of his men, for even now he would not relax his vigilance.

Manuel shrugged, rolled a cigarette, and looked about. His companions had crawled beneath several of the wagons, where they lay in the shade smoking, or already dozing. As far as he could see the land lay rollingly level, dotted with small bushes, not one of which would have offered concealment to anything larger than a jack rabbit. The sun was very hot and the shade beneath the wagons looked inviting to Manuel. He walked along the edge of the teams to the rearmost one and then back again. Glancing beneath a certain wagon he saw the captain curled up in sleep.

41

The guard walked all around the twenty wagons, looking off as far as he could. There were only Indians to fear and there were none in sight. Jesus Garcia had said that there was not an Apache within three hundred miles and Jesus was a famous Indian fighter. He had fought the Apaches and the Yaquis both. Manuel yawned and crawled beneath a wagon, just to finish his cigarette in the shade.

The mules had settled down to rest, sensible as mules always are. The men dozed, even Manuel, though he had not meant to. Before there were ears to hear there could not have lain upon the earth a deeper silence. There seemed no life—but there was. Within twenty feet of Manuel a pair of eager, savage eyes appraised him. Within a radius of two hundred feet eight other pairs of eager, savage eyes watched the dozing forms of the unconscious prey.

Lying prone, completely buried in the sand, except their eyes, their bows hidden beneath cleverly held bushes, seven warriors and two youths awaited the moment of attack. From the hills, a mile away, another warrior watched. He would come leaping down to battle when the attack was made. All day he had been following and watching the train, ready to warn his fellows of any unforeseen danger, or inform them of a deviation from the assumed plans of the quarry; but there had been no change. The train had moved as though ordered by Geronimo.

Manuel slept and dreamed of a soft-eyed senorita in Hermosillo. Geronimo moved and the sand fell from his painted naked body as he rose noiselessly to his feet. Eight other grim figures arose from scattered beds of sand. At a sign from Geronimo they crept forward to surround the train.

The mules commenced to move restlessly. One of them snorted as a brave approached it. Geronimo held his lance above his head; from nine throats issued the blood-curdling war whoop of the Apaches. Manuel awoke and scrambled from beneath the wagon, fumbling with his rifle. A young Indian leaped toward him and as the Mexican raised his weapon an arrow from the bow of Shoz-Dijiji, the Black Bear, transfixed his heart.

In old Hermosillo tears would come to the soft eyes of a senorita. Far to the north, near the headwaters of the Gila, the fire of savage pride would burn in the big, dark eyes of Ish-kay-nay when she heard of the valor of her playfellow.

The Mexicans, utterly surprised, had no chance. Confused, startled, seeing Indians in front of them they backed from beneath the wagons only to receive lances and arrows in their backs from the Indians darting in and out between the wagons of the train. Curses and screams, mingled with the savage cries of the Apaches, added to the bewilderment of the freighters who had not died with the first volley. There were but nine Apaches, yet to the handful of men who survived the first onslaught there seemed to be Indians everywhere, so quickly did the savage warriors move from point to point, driving home a lance here, speeding an arrow there, or grappling hand-to-hand as they plunged their knives into the bodies of the foe.

The captain of the train, bleeding, staggered to his feet from beneath the wagon in the shade of which he had been sleeping. As he arose he saw a huge buck leaping toward him with bloody knife upraised. Clubbing his rifle the Mexican swung the stock down upon the warrior's head and as the Indian collapsed at his feet he whipped his six-shooter from its holster and stood at bay.

A few yards from him a stalwart Apache was on the point of driving his lance through the chest of Jesus Garcia who had fought Apaches and Yaquis all his life and knew that there was not an Indian within three hundred miles. The captain raised his weapon and leveled it full at the back of the Indian. Thus close was Geronimo to death; and then a young Apache hurled himself violently upon the captain of the train and the two went down together. It was Shoz-Dijiji who had intervened to save the war chief's life. Two warriors saw the act—one of them was Juh.

Rolling upon the ground the white man and the Indian lad struggled; the one to use his firearm, the other to prevent that and to drive his knife home. Shoz-Dijiji was strong for his age, but he was no match for the Mexican except in agility; but he had one advantage in a hand-to-hand struggle that the Mexican did not possess—he was naked and his body was slippery with grease.

Shoz-Dijiji clung to the pistol wrist of his antagonist, while the other grasped the boy's forearm in an effort to prevent him from driving his knife home. Rolling over and over the Mexican finally succeeded in getting on top of the Apache. Slowly he forced his weapon toward the boy's head.

Shoz-Dijiji, struggling but making no outcry, thought that his hour had struck; yet he did not relax his efforts, rather he redoubled them to wrench free his knife hand. He saw the finger of the Mexican pressing upon the trigger of the six-shooter as the muzzle of the weapon drew gradually in line with his forehead; then he gave a final terrific tug at the arm of his enemy just as the latter fired.

The report deafened Shoz-Dijiji, the powder burned his brow; but at the same instant he wrenched his wrist free from the slipping clutch of the Mexican and drove his blade home between the other's shoulders. The man uttered a hoarse scream and fired again; but the shock and the pain of the wound rendered this shot but the result of the spasmodic clutching of his fingers and the bullet went into the ground beside Shoz-Dijiji's head.

Again and again the quick knife of the Be-don-ko-he was plunged home. The body of the Mexican writhed, his agonized eyes glared down from his contorted face upon the savage beneath him, he struggled once again to level his weapon and then he slumped forward upon Shoz-Dijiji.

The youth wriggled from beneath the dead body of his adversary, leaped to his feet and looked about him. The battle was over; its grim aftermath was being enacted. A few of the Mexicans, less fortunate than their companions, still lived. Upon these Geronimo, Juh and their fellows wrought hideously. Gripped, seemingly, by a cold, calculating frenzy of ferocity, that in another day and among a more enlightened race would have passed for religious zeal, they inflicted unspeakable torture upon the dying and nameless indignities upon the dead that would have filled with envy the high minded Christian inquisitors of the sixteenth century.

Shoz-Dijiji searching for loot upon the dead was conscious of the orgy of blood about him, but if it aroused any marked emotion within him his face did not reflect it. As he removed a cartridge belt from a Mexican the man moved and opened his eyes. The Apache shoved the sharpened quartz of his lance through the man's heart and resumed his search for plunder. He did not torture; he did not mutilate; but he was not deterred therefrom through any sense of compassion. He felt none. These were the enemies of his people.

They would have slain him had they had the opportunity. It was only fear or caution that prevented them and their kind from hunting down him and his kind and exterminating them; and it was through torture and mutilation that the Apache kept green in the hearts of his enemies both fear and caution. To most of them it was merely a well-reasoned component of their science of war, which is, after all, but saying that it was a part of their religion. To Geronimo it was something more.

VI

THE OATH OF GERONIMO

AROUSED by the shouts, the shots and the scent of the savages, the mules had, during the battle, staged a divertissement of their own. Some had kicked themselves free of restraining leather while others had but entangled themselves the more. Many were down.

Their taste for blood temporarily glutted, or for lack of more blood to spill, the Apaches turned their attention to the mules. While some cut loose those that were down, others rounded up those that were loose. In the meantime Geronimo and Juh had inspected the contents of the wagons which contained a general store of merchandise consigned to many a small merchant in the villages of northern Sonora.

Selecting what met their fancy or the requirements of their wild, nomadic life, they packed their spoils of war upon the backs of the captured mules and set out in a northeasterly direction toward the Sierra Madre. All that afternoon and all of the following night they pushed rapidly on until they emerged upon the eastern slopes of the Sierra Madre and looked down upon Chihuahua. Not until then did Geronimo order camp and a rest. A hundred miles behind them the ashes of the burned wagon train still smoldered. Ten miles in his rear a single scout watched the rear trail from a commanding peak and far ahead another scout overlooked Chihuahua.

Around the camp fire that day, while the mules browsed the lush grasses of a mountain meadow, the warriors recounted boastfully their deeds of derring-do.

Geronimo, sullen and morose, sat apart. Shoz-Dijiji, the camp duties of the neophyte completed, lay stretched in rest beside his savage sire. Geronimo, puffing at a cigarette, looked down at the boy.

"Shoz-Dijiji has done well," he said. These were the first words of approval that had fallen upon the youth's ears since he had taken the war trail. He remained silent. Geronimo puffed upon his cigarette before he spoke again. "Juh says that Shoz-Dijiji has a heart of water; that he did not join the other braves in torturing the wounded or mutilating the dead."

"Shoz-Dijiji killed three of the enemy," replied the youth; "one

45

in a hand-to-hand fight. The coyote attacks the wounded and devours the dead. Which is braver?"

"You saw me after the battle," said Geronimo. "Am I a coyote?"

"You are a brave man," replied Shoz-Dijiji simply. "There is no one braver than Geronimo. Therefore I cannot understand why you waste your time with the dead and the wounded. These, I should think, you would leave to the squaws and the children. I, Shoz-Dijiji, take no pleasure in fighting with a dead man who cannot harm me. I should not think that Geronimo, who is so much braver than Shoz-Dijiji, would find pleasure in it."

"Listen, my son, to the words of Geronimo," said the war chief. "But seventeen times had the rains fallen upon me when I was admitted to the warrior class. Then I was a Ned-ni, as my fathers before me had been; but I loved Alope, the slender daughter of No-po-so of the Be-don-ko-he and she loved me. I gave No-po-so the many ponies that he had asked for Alope and took her with me. Then it was that I was adopted into the tribe of my good wife. I became a Be-don-ko-he.

"Three children came to us in the twelve years that followed and we were happy. There was peace between us and the tribes that were our neighbors. We were at peace with the Mexican towns in Chihuahua and Sonora.

"Happy, carefree, contented, the Be-don-ko-he, with all their women and their children, went down through Sonora toward Casa Grande to trade, but before we reached our destination we stopped at the Mexican village which we called Kas-ki-yeh, making our camp just outside the town.

"I had brought my mother with me, as well as Alope and our three children. With the other women and children they remained in camp under the protection of a few warriors while the balance of the braves went daily into the town to trade.

"Thus we had been living in peace and fancied security for several days when one evening as we were returning to camp we were met by several of our women and children. Their burning eyes reflected the sorrow and righteous anger that blazed within their breasts as they told us that during our absence Mexican troops had attacked our camp, slain the warriors that had been left to guard it, run off our ponies, burned our supplies, stolen our weapons and murdered many of our women and children.

"Mangas Colorado, chief of the Ned-ni, who was with us with a few of his people, was the ranking war chief and to him we turned now, for this was war. He told us to separate and hide until darkness had fallen, and this we did, assembling again in a thicket by the river. Then it was, when all had come, that I discovered for

46

the first time that my aged mother, my young wife, my three small children were among the slain.

"Without ponies, without weapons, our force reduced, surrounded by the enemy and far within his country, we were in no position to give battle. In silence and in darkness, therefore, we took up the long trail toward our own country, leaving our dead upon the field.

"Stunned by the sorrow that had overwhelmed me I followed behind the retreating tribe, just within hearing distance of the soft footfalls of moccasined feet. For two days and nights of forced marching I did not eat, I did not speak, and no one spoke to me— there was nothing to say.

"At last we arrived at our own kunh-gan-hay. There was the tepee that I had made for Alope, a tepee of buffalo hides. There were the bear robes, the lion skins, the other trophies of the chase that I had placed there for her. There were the little decorations of beads and drawn work on buckskin made by Alope's own slender fingers. There were the many pictures that she had drawn upon the walls of our home, and there were the playthings of our little ones.

"I burned them all. Also I burned my mother's tepee and destroyed all her property. It was then I took an oath to be revenged upon the Mexicans, to kill them wherever I found them, to give them no quarter and to show them no mercy.

"My mother, Alope, our three children have been avenged many times over, but the end is not yet. Now, perhaps, Shoz-Dijiji too will see the same pictures of the mind that Geronimo sees when the war trail crosses the path of the Mexicans—an old woman and a young woman lying in their blood, three little children huddled together in terror before the bullets or the gun butts of the Mexican soldiers stilled their sobs forever."

The wrinkled war chief arose and walked silently away. In silence Shoz-Dijiji sat—in silence and in thought.

And all during the long, arduous marches that followed he thought upon what Geronimo had told him until he too came to hate the enemies of his people with a bitterness that was but to be increased with each closer association with them, whether in war or in peace; but Shoz-Dijiji discriminated less between Mexicans and Americans than did Geronimo, for he knew that upon the whole the former had sinned against them less than the latter.

Always watching for attack from in front, for pursuit from the rear, the Apaches drove the laden mules northward toward home, keeping as much to inaccessible mountains as the limitations of the mules permitted; passing the few habitations that lay in their way silently by night, with the single exception of an isolated Mexican ranch not far from the border. This they attacked by day, slaying its owner, his wife and children.

Again Shoz-Dijiji and Gian-nah-tah conducted themselves well, thus having two engagements to their credit of the four necessary before they could be accepted into the warrior class; but again Shoz-Dijiji abstained from torture or mutilation, though he watched Juh, the butcher, with interest, if nothing more.

The meager loot from the pitiful Mexican home they loaded upon a spare mule, set fire to the interior of the adobe house and continued their way, leaving the wounded but conscious Mexican staked out upon a bed of cactus within sight of the mutilated remains of his family, to die of thirst.

As they passed on toward the farther hills Shoz-Dijiji saw a coyote giving them a wide berth as it slunk down toward the ranch.

That night they crossed the border into New Mexico and camped in timbered mountains by a running spring. Here they killed a mule and feasted, for at last they felt reasonably safe from pursuit.

A few days later they came to their home camp and that night there was dancing and feasting in honor of the victorious warriors and a great deal of boastful recounting of valorous deeds and displaying of loot. Another mule was killed and cooked and presents were given to each member of the tribe. It was a memorable night. Tomorrow the work of the squaws would commence, for all the remaining mules must be killed, their meat jerked, their hides cured and the meat packed away in them for future use.

Little Ish-kay-nay, cross-legged upon the ground, tore at a large piece of mule meat with her strong, white teeth. A lock of glossy black hair fell across her face and tickled her nose. She pushed it back with a greasy hand.

But if her teeth were occupied with the feast her eyes were not— they followed the figure of a handsome youth who moved about with the swagger of a warrior, though it was noticeable that he kept out of the paths of the warriors, swaggering most where the squaws and the children might see.

Closer and closer to Ish-kay-nay his wanderings led him, yet he seemed quite unconscious of her presence, until presently, without a word, he came and squatted at her side. He did not speak. Ish-kay-nay did not speak. Perhaps each wondered at the change that had come over their relations. When the youth had gone away a few weeks before they had been playfellows. There had never been reserve between them. Ish-kay-nay had seemed like another boy to Shoz-Dijiji.

Now she seemed different. It seemed to Shoz-Dijiji that he was

48

almost afraid of her. To Ish-kay-nay there seemed a difference, too, but, being a woman, she was less mystified than Shoz-Dijiji and she was not afraid. She must only appear to be afraid.

Presently, timorously apparently, she extended her piece of mule meat toward him and with his teeth he tore off a mouthful. Enjoined from speech by necessity they sat there, side by side, chewing upon the tough and fibrous flesh.

Ish-kay-nay looked up from beneath her tousled shock, caught his eye and smiled. Then she looked down quickly and giggled. Shoz-Dijiji grinned and leaned a little closer until his naked shoulder touched hers. Again Ish-kay-nay looked up to smile, and down to giggle, shrugging her shapely shoulders.

Laboriously the youth untied a soiled bundle that he had carried for many days fastened to his loin cloth. It was wrapped in a bit of the tail of a cotton shirt that Manuel, the freighter, had bought in Guaymas.

A vile odor pervaded it, an odor that waxed in insolence and insistence as Shoz-Dijiji, with exaggerated deliberation, slowly unwrapped the package, while Ish-kay-nay, now leaning quite brazenly against him, watched with increasing interest. Neither appeared to note the odor which arose like material matter as the youth threw aside the last fold of cloth and held up to the girl's admiring gaze three putrid scalps.

"I, Shoz-Dijiji, have slain the enemies of my people," he said. "Upon the war trail with the warriors of my tribe I have slain them and here is the proof."

"Shoz-Dijiji will soon be a great warrior," whispered Ish-kay-nay, snuggling closer.

The boy opened the buckskin bag in which he kept his treasures. From it he drew a silver crucifix and a rosary. "Take these, Ish-kay-nay," he said. "Shoz-Dijiji took them in battle for Ish-kay-nay."

The eyes of the little savage maiden were wells of gratitude and pride, and as Shoz-Dijiji slipped an arm about her she looked up into his face and pressed closer to him. Now she did not giggle, for the light of a great understanding had suddenly flooded the consciousness of Ish-kay-nay.

For some time they sat there in silence, oblivious of the yells of the dancers, the beating of the es-a-da-ded, wrapped in the dawning realization of the wonder that had come into their lives. It was Shoz-Dijiji who first spoke.

"Ish-kay-nay will soon be a woman."

"At the next moon," replied the girl.

"Twice again must Shoz-Dijiji take the war trail with the braves

49

of his tribe before he can become a warrior," continued the youth. "Not until then may he tie his pony before the tepee of Ish-kay-nay, to await her answer to his suit. Ish-kay-nay is beautiful. Many warriors will desire her. Already has Shoz-Dijiji seen them looking at her. Will Ish-kay-nay wait for Shoz-Dijiji?"

"Until Chigo-na-ay gives forth no heat and the waters cease to run Ish-kay-nay will wait," whispered the girl.

DURING the month that followed the tribe travelled to a small salt lake that lies in the Gila Mountains, and there replenished its supply of salt. There were Navajos there, too, and a small band of Pimos, but there was no fighting, for such is the unwritten law of the Indians who have come hither for ages after their salt.

Even the birds and the beasts are safe here, for no creature may be killed upon its sacred shore. Here the gossip of the wild country passed from mouth to mouth, the braves traded or gambled, the squaws recovered the salt, and when the supply was garnered each tribe took up its separate way in safety back to its own country.

Shortly after they reached home the father of Ish-kay-nay, being a man of importance and considerable means, sent runners to the Apache tribes living nearest them, inviting all to a great dance and feast in honor of the coming of his daughter into the full bloom of womanhood, for Ish-kay-nay was fourteen and no longer a child.

For days the preparations went forward. The young bucks grinned and giggled at Ish-kay-nay, who tittered and hid her eyes behind her hand. And Shoz-Dijiji laughed in his blanket.

The roasted mescal had been mixed with water and allowed to ferment. Other pulpy sections of the maguey were being steamed in rock-lined pits, the stones in which had first been superheated with leaping, crackling greasewood fires before a layer of maguey was laid upon them and covered with wet leaves and grasses, upon which was laid a second layer of maguey, another layer of leaves and grasses, thus alternating until the pit was filled and the whole covered tightly over with earth from which protruded several of the long bayonet spikes of the mescal, the lower ends of which were embedded in the roasting pulp.

For three days had the maguey been cooking. The tribes were gathered. The fermented mescal was ready and, lest their hospitality be impeached, Ish-kay-nay's mother had brewed an ample supply of tizwin against the needs of the occasion. The Yuma slave woman cooked tortillas by a fire of her own making. There were jerked venison, lion, bear and beef; fresh turkey, grouse and mule; there were cakes of the meal of ground mesquite beans; there was the sun-dried fruit of the Spanish bayonet.

During the afternoon the squaws were engaged in the final

50

preparations for the feast; the braves, with mirror and pigment, were making themselves gorgeous for the ensuing nights of dancing, feasting and celebration, or, the painting done, arraying themselves in their finest buckskin, beaded, and silver or turquoise hung; placing necklaces, often to the number of a dozen, about their savage necks; adjusting earrings of silver or turquoise.

Little Ish-kay-nay was being prepared, too. She had donned a new and elaborately beaded robe of buckskin, the skirt of which was fringed with tiny silver bells, as were the sides of her high moccasins; and she was hung heavy with barbaric necklaces, some of which merely encircled her throat, while others fell below her waist.

Much of her wealth of silver and turquoise was hidden by the long, heavy fringe that fell from the edges of her voluminous sleeves and, encircling her skirt above her knees, swept the ground about her richly beaded moccasins; but there was enough in evidence to fix the wealth and social status of her sire.

Lengthening shadows heralded the coming of the guests. By ones and twos and threes they came, Chi-hen-ne, White Mountain, Chi-e-a-hen, Cho-kon-en and Ned-ni, to the camp of the Be-don-ko-he, to celebrate the coming of Ish-kay-nay, the bud, into the full flower of womanhood. A full September moon shone down upon them as they gathered about the open space from which the grass had been cut for the dancing. The potent mescal and tizwin was passed freely among them.

In nearby tepees the braves who were to start the dance put the last touches to their toilets. In a great lodge at one side of the dance ground the chief men of the six tribes assembled and there too sat Ish-kay-nay, looking very small; but, being Ish-kay-nay, neither overawed nor fearful. With poise and dignity she sat among the great, but doubtless in her elfin heart she was laughing at some of the grim old chieftains, as youth, the world over, is prone to laugh at age.

The squaws had drawn the bayonet stalks from the roasting maguey and sampling the lower ends had found them cooked to a nicety. Now they were uncovering the feast. A fire was burning in the center of the space reserved for the dancing, and at one side a dried hide had been laid upon the ground. About this sat several old warriors armed with long, tough sticks. Gently they began beating upon the surface of the bull hide. Just behind them two other old warriors smote es-a-da-deds. Ish-kay-nay's father began to sing in time to the beating of the crude drums, his voice rising and falling monotonously as he chanted of the beauty of Ish-kay-nay, of her docility, of her strength, of her many accomplishments. Gradually

51

the guests joined in, chanting in unison with him a wordless chant that drowned out the balance of the list of Ish-kay-nay's attractions.

Suddenly there burst from the tepees at the head of the dance ground a series of blood-curdling whoops and yells. The beating of the drums increased in tempo and volume until the sound rolled forth in thunderous waves. From several tepees young men sprang, leaping high in air, turning, twisting, bending, whooping. Onto the dance ground they rushed, circling the central fire—weird, grotesque, barbaric figures disguised beneath the heads and skins of bear and deer and buffalo and lion.

Four times about the fire they danced when other warriors armed with lances, bows and arrows sprang upon the dance ground and circling the other dancers threatened them with their weapons. Unintimidated the beasts danced on until at last the hunters threw down their weapons.

At this signal the young women of the tribes joined in the dance. As the first of them ran upon the field the young bucks gave voice to a wild yell that rolled out across the still Arizona night to reverberate and echo in the gloomy canyons and gorges of the moon-mysteried mountains that hemmed them about. They crouched, they leaped, they shook their shoulders and their hips as they formed a circle about the fire, facing outward, as the girls took their places in an outer circle, each girl opposite and facing a warrior.

The drums boomed, the dancers bent double, whirled about first upon one foot and then upon the other. The men advanced, the girls retreated to the outer edge of the dance ground. Among them, grotesque, painted, decked out in the finery of their most gorgeous medicine headdress, their finest izze-kloths, whirling their tzi-ditindes, the izze-nantans whirled and leaped and danced, sprinkling the sacred hoddentin upon the youths and maidens.

Nakay-do-klunni was there with Nan-ta-do-tash and many another famous medicine man of the six tribes of the Apaches, speaking volumes for the wealth and power of the father of little Ish-kay-nay. Now the men retreated, backing toward the fire, and the girls advanced, and thus, forward and back, they danced for hours, chanting the sacred songs of their people, doing honor to Ish-kay-nay.

And all the time the girl remained in the great lodge, taking no part in the festivities and catching but an occasional glimpse of what was going on without. At the end of the fourth night the food was gone, the mescal and the tizwin had been consumed, the dancers were exhausted and the six tribes repaired to their several camps to sleep off the effects of their prolonged orgy. On the following day

Ish-kay-nay's eyebrows were carefully plucked—the last official symbol of her emergence from childhood to the marriage market. A month later her eye lashes would be pulled out.

Shoz-Dijiji was not happy. He had had no part in the festivities, other than a free hand at the food, and he had tried to smoke—with dire results. This he might have done long before, having killed big game and won the right to smoke like a grown man; but he had not cared to until recently. Seeing Ish-kay-nay stepping suddenly from childhood to womanhood had awakened within him, or rather had stimulated within him an already overwhelming desire to appear mature.

From the tepee of Geronimo he had taken a few leaves of tobacco and these he rolled in the dried leaf of an oak. With an ember from a camp fire he lighted his primitive cigarette, and for several minutes he derived great satisfaction from parading nonchalantly about, puffing clouds of smoke to the moon; but shortly he crawled away out of sight and lay down behind a bush. For a while he was quite helpless, but presently he was able to unwrap his tzi-daltai, and to it he prayed that the bad spirit that had entered his stomach with the smoke be driven out. He prayed for a long time, until he fell asleep; and when he awoke he knew that his medicine was strong medicine, for the sickness was gone, leaving him only a little weak and a bit wobbly upon his feet.

Perhaps the sickness helped to make Shoz-Dijiji unhappy, but there were other causes, too. One of them was the attitude of the young warriors toward Ish-kay-nay, and that of some of the old warriors, as well. Never before had Shoz-Dijiji realized how wonderful and how desirable was Ish-kay-nay, and he saw that other youths and men thought that she was desirable. Once, shortly after the great feast, he saw ten ponies tied before her tepee, and among them was the war pony of Juh, the chief of the Ned-ni.

For four days he watched them standing there, as their owners watched them; but Ish-kay-nay did not come forth and feed any one of them or lead one to water, and at the end of the fourth day, disgruntled, the disappointed swains came and took away their ponies. After that Shoz-Dijiji was happier and when it was dark, that very night, he found Ish-kay-nay and sat down beside her and held her hand and heard her say over again that she would wait for him— forever.

VII

RAIDED

ONE day as Shoz-Dijiji squatted beside Geronimo listening to the great chief's tales of the war trail a runner came and stopped before them.

"Geronimo," he said, "I am sent by the officers of the white soldiers. They want you to come to their camp. They have sent a runner to Victorio also, and he is coming."

"What do the chiefs of the white soldiers want of Geronimo and Victorio?" demanded the chief.

"I do not know," replied the runner.

"Perhaps they are calling a council," suggested Geronimo.

"Perhaps," replied the runner, an Apache scout in the service of the government.

"Tell them Geronimo will come," said the chief, and the scout turned and trotted away, disappearing among the trees below the camp.

"Fetch my pony, Shoz-Dijiji," said Geronimo.

"And mine?" asked the youth.

Geronimo smiled and grunted an affirmative and the lad was gone after the two ponies. When he returned Geronimo was ready and together they rode down the mountainside in the direction of the little town near which the soldiers were camped.

Early the following morning they saw a small band of Indians moving in the same direction as were they, and evidently toward the camp of the white soldiers which lay beside the village of Hot Springs which they could already see in the distance.

"Victorio," grunted Geronimo, nodding his head.

Shoz-Dijiji nodded. However the two approached the other party, as their trails converged, with careful wariness, and it was not until they had actually recognized individual members of the band and been recognized in turn that they finally joined them.

The two chiefs rode together, exchanging occasional monosyllables, but for the greater part of the time in silence. Shoz-Dijiji took the station befitting a youth among warriors and rode in the rear and the dust. At the edge of town the party was met by soldiers, two companies of scouts, and before Geronimo or Victorio could realize their intentions the party was surrounded, disarmed

54

and arrested. Surprised, chagrined and angry the Apaches were conducted to military headquarters, and for the first time Shoz-Dijiji came into close contact with the pindah lickoyee.

Closely surrounded by armed soldiers the Apaches were herded into a tent where several officers were seated behind two camp tables. Ignoring his guards Geronimo strode forward and faced the officers across the tables.

"Why have the soldiers done this to Geronimo and his friends?" he demanded. "You sent for Geronimo as a friend and he came as a friend. Is this the way to treat a friend?"

The senior officer turned to a Mexican standing near him. "What does he say?" he demanded.

The Mexican, in turn, addressed a half-breed squatting at his side. "What does he say?" he asked in Spanish. The half-breed translated Geronimo's words into Spanish and the Mexican translated them into English for the senior officer.

"Tell him it is because he left Apache Pass without permission," replied the officer. "Ask him why he did this," and again the Mexican translated the officer's words into Spanish and the half-breed translated them from Spanish to Apache. Thus the entire proceedings were carried out. Perhaps the translations were accurate—perhaps not. At any rate the principals in the matter did not know.

Geronimo mused over the question before he replied. Then he addressed himself directly to the senior officer, ignoring the interpreters. "I do not think that I ever belonged to those soldiers at Apache Pass," he said, "or that I should have asked them where I might go. This is my country. I have lived here all my life. It is the country that Usen gave to the Apaches when he created them. It has always belonged to us. Why should we ask the soldiers of the white-eyes for permission to go from one part of our own country to another part?

"We have tried to live in peace with the white-eyes. We even tried to stay at Apache Pass when they asked us to do so; but the white-eyes do not know the ways of the Apaches as do the chiefs of the Apaches. They did not know what they asked. The six tribes of the Apaches cannot all live together in peace. The young men quarrel. This we knew would happen, yet we tried to live together because we were told that it was the wish of the Great White Chief.

"Some of the young men got drunk on whiskey that was sold to them by a white-eyed man. They fought and some were killed. We, who are the chiefs of our people, we, who are responsible for their welfare and happiness, held a council and there we all agreed that the tribes could no longer live in peace together.

"The Chi-hen-ne and Be-don-ko-he have always been friendly and so Victorio and I quietly withdrew together with our people. We did not think this was wrong. Our hearts were not wrong. That is all. Geronimo has spoken. Now let us return to our homes."

The officer questioned Victorio and several other Indians. He asked about each one present and Shoz-Dijiji heard himself mentioned, heard the half-breed say that he was but a youth and not yet a warrior, for Shoz-Dijiji understood some Spanish. Now he realized that it would be advantageous to understand the language of the pindah lickoyee as well.

The proceedings did not last long. The officers issued some orders to the soldiers and the Apaches were herded from the tent. Geronimo and seven other Apaches were taken to the guardhouse and placed in chains. Victorio and the others, including Shoz-Dijiji, were released; but the youth did not wish to leave his father. With that mixture of timidity and courage which often marks the actions of creatures of the wild in the presence of white men, Shoz-Dijiji, keeping at a distance, followed Geronimo to the guardhouse.

He saw the Indians disappear within, he saw the door closed. He wondered what they were going to do with his father and his friends, these white-eyed men whose actions he could no more understand than he could their language. He crept to a window and looked in. His pupils dilated with horror at the thing he saw; they were placing great chains upon Geronimo, upon the chief of the Be-don-ko-he, upon the war chief of all the Apaches, and fastening him to the wall like a wild beast.

Shoz-Dijiji shuddered. The humiliation of it! And the hideous injustice. Savage that he was, Shoz-Dijiji sensed keenly and felt acutely the injustice, for he knew that Geronimo did not know why he was being punished. He knew that the soldiers had said that it was because he had left Apache Pass, but to Shoz-Dijiji as well as to Geronimo, that was worse than no reason at all since they both knew that it had been the right thing to do.

Shoz-Dijiji, through the window, heard Geronimo ask the soldiers why he was being chained in the guardhouse; but they did not understand him. One, who was quite a joker, mimicked the old war chief, making the other soldiers laugh, thus demonstrating beyond cavil the natural superiority of the white race over these untutored children of the wild who sat now in majestic silence, their immobile faces giving no hint of the thoughts that passed within their savage brains, or the sorrows within their hearts.

Doubtless, had their positions been reversed, the Apaches would have tortured the soldiers; but it is a question as to whether they could have inflicted upon the white men any suffering more real, more terrible, than are imprisonment and ridicule to an Indian.

As Shoz-Dijiji watched through the guardhouse window, his whole being was so occupied by the numbing terror of what he saw within that he did not hear the approach of a white soldier from his rear, nor was he conscious of any other presence about him until a heavy hand was laid upon his shoulder and he was wheeled roughly about.

"What the hell are you doing here, you dirty Siwash?" demanded the trooper, and at the same time he gave Shoz-Dijiji a shove that sent him sprawling in the dust.

Shoz-Dijiji did not understand the white man's words. He did not understand why he had been attacked. All he knew was that, his heart filled with sorrow, he had been watching the humiliation of his father; but as he arose slowly from the dust he became conscious of a new force within him that crowded sorrow into the background—a deep, implacable hatred of the pindah lickoyee. Through level eyes, his face an imperturbable mask, he looked at the white soldier and saw that he was heavily armed. About the guardhouse were other armed soldiers. Shoz-Dijiji turned and walked away. Apache-like he bided his time.

In the camp of his people Shoz-Dijiji took up again his accustomed life, but he was not the same. The last vestige of youth had fallen from him. Quiet, serious, even morose he was, and more and more often did he spend nights and days upon end in the high places, praying and making big medicine, that he might be strong against the enemies of his people.

He talked with Gian-nah-tah about the wrongs that the pindah lickoyee would inflict upon the Shis-Inday. He visited Victorio and talked much with that savage, terrible old warrior, for Shoz-Dijiji wanted to know "why." No one seemed to be able to enlighten him. Usen had made this country for the Apaches, of that they were all quite sure; but why Usen had sent the white-eyes, no one could tell him. Victorio thought that Usen had nothing to do with it; but that some bad spirits who hated Usen were really responsible.

"The bad spirits have sent the white-eyed men to kill the Apaches," he explained, "so that Usen will have no one to guard him. Then they will be able to kill Usen."

"Then we should kill the enemies of Usen," said Shoz-Dijiji.

"It is right to kill them," said Victorio. "Do they not kill us?"

Shoz-Dijiji knew that they did. He knew that when he was hunting, deep in his own country, he had ever to keep an alert eye open for wandering white men—hunters, prospectors, cowboys, soldiers—scarce one of whom but would shoot him first and inquire into his friendliness afterward, if at all.

In primitive places news travels with a celerity little short of miraculous. Thus it was that the day that Geronimo was transferred to the guardhouse at San Carlos the fact was known to the Be-don-ko-he in their hidden camp, deep in inaccessible mountains. Shoz-Dijiji spoke to Morning Star, wife of Geronimo, the only mother he had ever known.

"Sons-ee-ah-ray," he said, "I, Shoz-Dijiji, go to be near my father, Geronimo. The hearts of the pindah lickoyee are bad. Perhaps they have taken him away to kill him."

"Go!" said Morning Star. "If the pindah lickoyee harm Geronimo return quickly and bring the word. Then, if the hearts of the Apache braves have not turned to water, they will go upon the war trail and drive the white-eyed men from the land of the Shis-Inday forever. If they do not, then the squaws will spit upon them and take their weapons from them and go upon the war trail in their places."

So Shoz-Dijiji set out alone and afoot for the fort at San Carlos. Deep in his heart was a purpose that he had not confided to Morning Star or to any other, not even to Ish-kay-nay when he had bid her farewell. In the high places Shoz-Dijiji had had much opportunity for thought and for reflection, and more and more during those solitary hours among the silent rocks and the murmuring pines there had been borne into his consciousness a realization of the fact that he had first vaguely comprehended at the trial of Geronimo at Hot Springs, that his people were handicapped in their struggle against the white-eyed oppressor by their inability to understand his language.

Shoz-Dijiji had recalled the night that he had lain close beside the parked wagon train of the Mexican freighters and overheard their plans for the ensuing days, and because he knew their language it had been possible for his people to profit by what he heard. How great might be his advantage upon similar occasions in the conflict with the whites, if he understood their tongue, he thoroughly realized. Imbued with this thought as well as a desire to be near his father and learn more of what the whites intended for Geronimo, the youth made his lonely way toward San Carlos.

With a handful of parched corn, a few strips of jerked venison and a primitive water bottle of horse gut, he trotted silently along his untracked way. Always alert for signs of the enemy, no sound escaped his trained ears; no broken twig, no down-pressed bunch of

58

grass, no turned stone escaped his watchful eyes; and all that he saw he read as quickly and as accurately as we read the printed page; but with this difference, possibly—Shoz-Dijiji understood what he read.

Here he saw where klij-litzogue, the yellow snake, had passed through the dust of the way an hour before; there was the spoor of shoz-lickoyee; and in the bottom of a parched canyon he saw signs of the pindah lickoyee. Two days before a white man had ridden down this canyon toward the plain upon the back of a mare with a white right hind foot and a black tail. All this Shoz-Dijiji read quickly from a spoor so faint that you or I would not have noticed it at all. But then, it was Shoz-Dijiji's business to know, as it is our business to know that if we ignore certain traffic signals at a crowded corner we may land in the receiving hospital.

On the second day Shoz-Dijiji crept to the summit of a low divide and looked down upon the frontier post of San Carlos, upon the straw-thatched buildings of adobe brick, upon the winding Gila and upon the straggling villages of the reservation Indians, and that night he slipped silently down among the shadows and merged with his people. There were many tribes there, but among them were Apaches whom Shoz-Dijiji knew, and these he sought, seeking word of Geronimo first. They told him that the chief was still chained in a guardhouse, but that he was well. What the white-eyes intended doing with him they did not know.

Shoz-Dijiji asked many questions and learned many things that night. With the braves he laughed at the white fools who fed the Apaches between raids while the blood of other white men was scarce dry upon them, and, who, while feeding them, sought to cheat them out of the bulk of the rations the Great White Chief had sent them; thus increasing their contempt for the whites, arousing their anger against them, and spurring them on to further outbreaks.

"Our women and our children are hungry," complained an old warrior, "and yet they will neither give us passes to go out on the hunting trail or issue us sufficient rations to sustain us. We see the agent growing rich and fat upon the money that should buy us beef. We see our war chief and our friends chained in prison. To make us content they wish to give us shovels and hoes and make us do the work of squaws. They wish us to go to school and learn the strange language of the white-eyes.

"We are men, we are warriors; it is not fit that men and warriors should do these things. It is our land, not theirs. Usen gave it to us and he gave the white-eyes other lands. Why do they not stay in the land that Usen gave them, as we have? We do not want them here."

Shoz-Dijiji heard a great deal of such talk, for the Indians, discontented, aired their grievances freely among themselves. They talked of little else, and the young bucks spoke continually of war. These matters did not, however, greatly excite Shoz-Dijiji. He knew that when the time came there would be war. There always was. What interested him more was the statement of the old warrior that the white-eyed men wished his people to learn their language. He spoke often upon this subject, asking many questions.

"You wish to learn the language of the pindah lickoyee?" demanded a scarred warrior who talked the loudest and the longest about war.

"Yes," admitted Shoz-Dijiji.

"That is labor," sneered the warrior. "The men of the Apaches do not labor. You should have been a squaw."

"The men of the Apaches make their own weapons wherewith to fight the enemies of their people, do they not?" inquired Shoz-Dijiji.

"That is the work of men, of warriors," exclaimed the other.

"The language of the white-eyes can be turned into a weapon against them if we understand it," said the youth. "Now they use it against us. That I saw at Hot Springs when Geronimo and the other warriors were made prisoners. It was all done with the talk of the white-eyes; no other weapon did they use. Had I known how to use that weapon—had Geronimo, or any other of us known—we might have defeated them, for we had the right upon our side."

"Shoz-Dijiji makes good talk," said an old man. "At the post they have a school where they wish us to send our children and to come ourselves to learn their language. There are but three children in this school and they are all orphans. If they had had parents they would not have been permitted to go. The pindah lickoyee will be glad to have you come."

And so it was that Black Bear attended the school of the pindah lickoyee and learned their strange language. He stayed and worked in the school after the class was dismissed that he might ask questions of the teacher and learn more rapidly. His teacher, the wife of an officer, pointed to him with pride and told her friends that the example set by Black Bear would probably do more toward pacifying and civilizing the Apaches than all the soldiers in the United States Army could accomplish.

"If they understand us they will learn to respect and love us," she said; "and they cannot understand us until they understand our language."

And to his people Shoz-Dijiji said: "The pindah lickoyee are fools and their tongue is the tongue of fools; but it is well to know it.

Already I have learned things about them that otherwise I could never have known, and when I take the war trail against them as a man there will be no arrow in my quiver with which I can inflict more harm upon them than with this—my knowledge of their language."

For three months Shoz-Dijiji attended school regularly, studied diligently, learned quickly. His teacher was transported into raptures whenever she had occasion to mention him in the presence of her friends, and that was often, as the topics of conversation at a frontier army post are meager at the best. Her husband was skeptical, as were all of the older officers.

"He's an Indian," they said, "and the only good Indian is a dead Indian."

Thus understandingly, sympathetically, has the Indian question been approached by many army men, and by practically all of the civilians of the frontiers. To have said: "He is an Indian. He stands in the way of our acquisition of his valuable possessions. Therefore, having no power to enforce his rights and being in our way, we will destroy him," would have been no more ruthless than the policy we adopted and cloaked with hypocrisy. It would have had the redeeming quality of honesty, and would have been a policy that the Apaches could have understood and admired.

One morning Shoz-Dijiji did not come to school. He never came again. His teacher made diligent inquiry which always ended against the dead wall of an Indian, "No savvy." She did not connect Black Bear's disappearance with the release of Geronimo from the guardhouse the previous afternoon, because she did not know that Black Bear was Geronimo's son.

She knew nothing about Black Bear. From her he had learned all that he sought to learn; from him she had learned nothing; for which there is just one good and sufficient reason—Black Bear was an Apache. Of all the great Indian tribes that have roamed North America none has been in contact with white men longer than the Apache, and of none is there less known.

Ugly, morose, vengeful, Geronimo came back to his people, and that same night they slipped away toward the south. Every member of the tribe was mounted and their meager belongings, their store of provisions, were packed upon the backs of spare ponies.

Shoz-Dijiji was happy. The three months spent at San Carlos under the petty restrictions of a semi-military regime had seemed an eternity of bondage to his free, wild nature. Now again he could breathe, out in the open where there were no fences, no walls, as far as the eye could reach, and the air was untainted by the odor of white men.

61

He looked up at the moon-silvered mountains and out across the dim, mysterious distance of the plain. He heard the old, familiar voices of the night, and her perfumes were sweet in his nostrils. He drank deep of it, filling his lungs. He wanted to leap into the air and dance and shout; but he only sat stolidly astride his pony, his face reflecting nothing of all that filled his heart.

Travelling by night, hiding by day, Geronimo led his people to a hidden valley, deep in the mountains, far from the trails and settlements of the pindah lickoyee. There they lived in peace and security for a long time, making occasional journeys into Mexico to trade, or to neighboring Indian tribes for the same purpose.

Shoz-Dijiji grew taller, stronger. Few warriors of the Be-don-ko-he could hurl a lance as far as he, and none could send an arrow with greater accuracy to its goal; he could out-run and out-jump them all, and his horsemanship brought a gleam of pride to the cruel, blue eyes of Geronimo.

The long period of peace broke down the discipline of the tribe and even astute old Geronimo nodded. An individualist in the extreme sense of the word, an Apache takes orders from no one except as it suits him to do so. Their chiefs are counsellors; they may not command. Only the war chiefs in time of battle or upon the war trail are vouchsafed anything approaching absolute authority. It is the ambition of every youth to become a warrior so that he may do whatever he wishes to do, without let or hindrance.

Thus lived the tribe in the dangerous insecurity and laxity of peace. No longer did the keen eyes of scouts watch the trails leading away into the lands of their enemies. For days at a time the ponies pastured without a guard.

It was upon such a day, following a successful hunt, that the warriors were dozing about the camp. Gian-nah-tah and Shoz-Dijiji, tiring of the monotony, had wandered away into the hills. They were moving quietly along, seeing everything, hearing everything, when the son of Geronimo stopped suddenly and raised his hand. Like a golden bronze by a master hand they stood motionless and silent. Faintly from afar came the rolling of distant thunder, scarcely heard. But Shoz-Dijiji and Gian-nah-tah knew that it was not thunder. Just for an instant they stood there listening and then both dropped almost simultaneously to the ground, pressing ears against the turf.

Shoz-Dijiji was the first to leap to his feet. "Return to camp, Gian-nah-tah," he said, "and tell Geronimo what we have heard."

"What is it, Shoz-Dijiji?" asked the other.

"The herd has been stampeded. They are running away from

camp—south, toward Chihuahua. Only enemies would run it off. Tell Geronimo that the Mexicans have raided us."

Gian-nah-tah wheeled about and raced down the mountainside, while Shoz-Dijiji clambered straight up toward a lofty point that would afford him a wide view of the country toward the south. His ear had told him that the ponies were running wildly; therefore they must be frightened. Nothing in these hills could so frighten those ponies as could mounted men urging them rapidly from the rear— that Shoz-Dijiji knew. The diminishing volume of the sound had told him that the ponies were moving away from him, toward the south. The rest was, of course, but shrewd inference.

From the summit he sought, he could see nothing but a cloud of dust receding down a canyon, and so he moved on after the retreating herd. For three hours he followed without catching a glimpse of ponies or thieves until he came out into the foothills and overlooked the plain beyond. Far out toward the south he saw just what he had expected to see, all the ponies and mules of the Be-don-ko-he. Driving them was a detachment of Mexican troopers and in their rear rode the balance of the company.

To follow was useless. He turned and trotted back toward camp. Halfway up the canyon he met Geronimo and some twenty braves already on the trail. Gian-nah-tah was with them. Shoz-Dijiji told Geronimo what he had seen, and when the party resumed the pursuit, not being forbidden, he fell in behind with Gian-nah-tah.

"Two more battles and we shall be warriors," whispered Shoz-Dijiji.

Far behind the mounted troopers, dogged, determined, trailed the twenty—grim and terrible.

VIII

VAQUEROS AND WARRIORS

DOWN into Sonora the trail of the raiders led them, but the Mexicans, versed in the ways of the Apaches, loitered not upon the trail. Pushing their stolen stock to the utmost of the endurance of man and beast they kept ahead of their pursuers. Yet to accomplish it they were compelled to average from sixty to seventy miles a day through rough mountains and across fiery, dust-choked flats, thirst-tortured, wearied, quirting on their jaded mounts in sullen effort to outdistance the avenging red demons that they never saw, but who experience, torture-won, told them followed relentlessly just below the northern horizon. Brave men, these, whose courage on countless savage, unsung fields deserves a fairer recognition than it has received at the hands of the chroniclers north of the Line.

Exhausted, half-starved, the troopers rode at last into a cattle ranch near Nacozari; where, after turning the stock over to a dozen cowboys, they were asleep almost before they could satisfy the pangs of hunger.

Twenty miles behind them, their deep chests rising and falling unhurriedly, trotted the twenty upon their trail. There were old men among them and youths yet unmatured, but nowhere was there sign of fatigue, though for three days and nights they had hung doggedly to the trail of mounted men, gaining in the last day almost all the distance they had lost while the horses of the Mexicans were fresh.

Just before dark they halted within sight of the ranch and from vantage points of concealment saw their herd grazing under the watchful eyes of the dozen vaqueros. Quenching their thirst in the nauseous, sun-heated contents of their septic water bottles, allaying their hunger with bits of dried meat, tough as leather and stinking to heaven, they waited. They were not resting, they were merely waiting.

Mighty men were these, as nearly immune to fatigue as human flesh may ever be, or ever has been. Some there were among them, however, who, feeling perhaps a hint of rebellion upon the part of overdriven muscles, cut switches from ready mesquite and lashed recalcitrant legs until they bled, scarifying them to renewed life and vitality.

Shoz-Dijiji was not of these. He had not tired. Prone behind a

64

little bush, chewing upon a bit of strength-giving carrion, his sober, unchanging eyes bored through the dusk down to the unsuspecting vaqueros and the herd. They held mostly upon a browsing pinto, Nejeunee, friend, as his name implied, pal, comrade, prized possession of this son of Geronimo. Shoz-Dijiji owned two other ponies. They, too, were there; but they were not to him as was Nejeunee.

The youth chafed to move forward to the battle. He glanced behind him in the direction of Geronimo who would give the signal for advance and attack. He saw that the old chief and the other warriors had removed their shirts and cotton drawers. They were stripped now to moccasins, G-strings, head handkerchiefs, and they were greasing their bodies and painting their faces. Shoz-Dijiji thrilled. The war paint—Ah! how it had always filled his brain with fire and his breast with savage emotions that he could not fathom, that he could only feel as they raised him to an exaltation, to a fanaticism of the spirit such as the old crusaders must have felt as they donned their armor to set their lances against the infidels. Deep within him smoldered the savage fires of his Caledonian ancestry that made him one with the grim crusaders of the past and with the naked descendants of the Athapascans preparing for battle.

The hearts of the crusaders were upheld by the holiness of their cause; the soldiers of the Sultan Saladin died defending Allah and the right; Usen looked down upon the Be-don-ko-he and was pleased. Who may judge where the right lay?

Geronimo sent a warrior to relieve Shoz-Dijiji that he might strip and prepare for battle. Dusk deepened into a moonless night canopied by a star-shot heaven so clear and close that the stars seemed friends that one might reach out and touch. The Apaches, lovers of Nature, sensed beauties that many a dull frontier clod of the usurping superior race lacked the soul to see. Even on the verge of battle they felt and acknowledged the wonders and beauties of the night, casting hoddentin to the heavens and the winds as they prayed to their amulets and consulted their phylacteries.

The time had come. The war chief had issued his orders. Each brave knew his position and his duties. One by one they crept from the concealment of the mesquite thicket behind which they had made their preparations. Below them and up wind was the herd. No bush was too small to offer them concealment as they crept down toward the enemy.

Half the band was to circle to the opposite side of the herd, which, being composed principally of Indian stock, would not be excited by the scent of Indians. Geronimo went with this detachment. At his signal the Apaches would attack simultaneously

65

upon all sides. Certain braves were to be the first to seize mounts and attempt to drive off the balance of the stock. Shoz-Dijiji was one of those chosen for this duty. He would rather have remained and fought, but the word of the war chief was law to Shoz-Dijiji.

Following the braves with Geronimo, the youth, belly to the ground, crept stealthily to the rear of the herd, giving the vaqueros a wide berth. The warriors, increasing their distances, spread out until a thin line entirely surrounded the Mexicans and their charges; then they closed in. The Apaches worked with almost the precision of trained troops but without word of command.

Geronimo saw a vaquero a few yards in front of him turn in his saddle and peer intently at the shrub behind which the war chief lay. For a long moment the Mexican watched intently; then, apparently satisfied, he looked in another direction. Geronimo took deliberate aim and pressed the trigger of his Springfield. There was a flash and roar. The Mexican fell forward upon his horse's neck.

Simultaneously the quiet of the night was blasted by a bedlam of hideous war whoops. From all sides, from all directions they fell upon the ears of the vaqueros. There was the cracking of rifles and the shouts and curses of men. Shoz-Dijiji, Gian-nah-tah and another rushed into the midst of the herd. The Black Bear whistled shrilly and Nejeunee, at a distance, half-frightened by the noise and confusion, about ready to break for liberty and safety, heard. Halting, he turned with up-pricked ears and looked back in the direction of the familiar sound. Again the youth whistled and there was an answering nicker from the stallion.

Arrows and lances and bullets flew thickly through the air. Only the fast movement of the participants, and the darkness, held down the casualties. The Mexicans, separated, surprised, outnumbered, readily assumed the attacking force much greater than it was, yet strove valiantly to protect the herd and hold it from stampede. The Apaches, profiting by the darkness, advantaging by the shrewd strategy of Geronimo, carried through their well-planned attack with whirlwind rapidity.

Shouldering through the frightened herd, Nejeunee galloped to his master. A vaquero, catching sight of the youth, wheeled his mount and bore down upon him. Shoz-Dijiji hurled his lance and missed as the other fired point-blank at him from a distance so close that the next stride of his horse brought him abreast the youthful brave. The powder from the six-shooter of his assailant burned Shoz-Dijiji's cheek as the bullet whizzed by his ear, and at the same instant the Apache leaped for the vaquero, caught his arm, and swung to the horse's rump behind the saddle of the Mexican.

The frightened horse leaped forward as its rider, dropping the

66

reins the better to defend himself, sought to rid himself of the savage Nemesis upon his back. At their side raced Nejeunee, harking to the low words of Shoz-Dijiji urging him on. About the neck of the Mexican went a sinewy left arm, a well-greased, muscular, copper-colored arm, as the Apache's right hand drew a hunting knife from its sheath.

As they flashed by them Geronimo and two other warriors saw and voiced their applause of the Black Bear in savage whoops of approbation. His black hair flying from beneath his head band, his muscles tensed to the exigencies of mortal combat, his black eyes flashing fierce hatred, Shoz-Dijiji with a forearm beneath his adversary's chin had forced back the latter's head until now they rode cheek to cheek while the knife of the Apache hovered above the back-stretched throat of the Mexican. For but an instant it hovered. Seeing, the terrified vaquero voiced a single shriek which ended in a bloody gurgle as the keen blade cut deep from ear to ear.

Slipping from the horse's rump clear of the falling corpse, Shoz-Dijiji leaped to Nejeunee's back and, bridleless, guided him in a circle that rounded the rear of the herd, where, whooping, yelling, he commenced the task of turning it toward the north, assisted by Gian-nah-tah and the warrior who had been detailed for this duty. One by one the other warriors of the party caught mounts from the milling, frightened herd—in itself a highly arduous and dangerous undertaking amid the flying heels and bared teeth of the half wild, wholly frightened animals—as the remaining vaqueros, believing themselves attacked by the full strength of the six Apache tribes raced for the camp of the soldiers. Of the twelve two were dead, and one, his horse shot from beneath him, rode behind a comrade.

Awakened by the shots and the war whoops the sleepy soldiers were stumbling to arms under the oaths and urgings of their officers as the ten vaqueros galloped into camp with as many excited versions of the attack and the battle as there were survivors. The commanding officer listened, asked questions, swore luridly when he discovered that not only all the stock that he had won from the Apaches in the face of torture, death and unspeakable hardship had been run off by the renegades, but all the horses of his command, as well as those belonging to the ranch, with the exception of the nine that had come back from the scene of battle.

Bad as this was it did not constitute his greatest concern, for if the Indians numbered but a fraction of what the vaqueros reported, their force was sufficient to wipe out his entire command; and it was not at all unlikely that, after starting the herd at a safe distance on the way toward Arizona, they would return in force and attack his camp. Thoughts of defense, therefore, were paramount to plans of pursuit, and the officer set about placing a strong guard about his position.

But no attack materialized. The Apaches did not reappear. They were far away upon the northern trail, urging their ponies to greater speed as they drove the captured herd ahead all during the long night. In their rear rode Geronimo, Shoz-Dijiji and another warrior to guard against a surprise attack by pursuers. Stopping often to watch and listen they fell far behind.

"Shoz-Dijiji did well," said Geronimo. "You are young, but already you have three battles to your credit—a fourth and the council of warriors can accept you. Geronimo is proud. He laughed when he saw you cut the throat of the Mexican. That was well done. Kill them, Shoz-Dijiji, kill them—always."

"But Geronimo does not always kill them," said the youth. "Sometimes Geronimo goes among them to trade, and laughs and jokes with them."

The war chief grunted. "That," said he, "is the wisdom of an old chief. Go among them and trade and laugh and make jokes so that when you come the next day to cut their throats they will not be prepared to resist you."

A simple, kindly soul was the old chief when compared with the diplomats of civilization who seek by insidious and false propaganda to break down the defenses of whole nations that they may fall easier prey to the attacks of their enemies. Yet ever will the name of Geronimo be held up to a horrified world as the personification of cruelty and treachery, though during his entire life fewer men died at the hands of the six tribes of the Apaches than fell in a single day of many an offensive movement during a recent war between cultured nations.

This was the first time that Shoz-Dijiji had been permitted to enter into conversation since the war party had left in pursuit of the Mexicans and so, while far from garrulous, he made the most of it, as he never tired of listening to the too infrequent tales of his sire, and tonight, as they rode side by side, he felt that Geronimo was in good humor and ripe for narrative.

"Shoz-Dijiji knows why Geronimo hates the Mexicans," said the youth, "and Shoz-Dijiji hates them, too—also, he hates the pindah lickoyee. But before the Mexicans murdered the mother of Geronimo and his wife and children, and the soldiers of the white-eyes slew the Apaches they had invited to have food with them, and before Mangas Colorado was treacherously murdered, did the Apaches have reason to hate the Mexicans and the white-eyes?"

"Many years ago," commenced Geronimo, "when Go-yat-thlay was yet a youth, El Gobernador del Chihuahua put a price upon the scalps of Apaches, just as the pindah lickoyee do upon the scalps of wolves. For each Apache scalp brought to him he offered to pay thirty dollars, nor was this for the scalps of warriors only, but included the scalps of women and children. They treated us even then you see, not like men but like wild beasts. But even this offer, large as it was, did not bring him many scalps of Apaches, for few there are who will hunt scalps who have scalps to lose and always, then as now, the name of the Apache turned the hearts of his enemies to water.

"But there was a pindah lickoyee called Gal-lan-tin whose heart was very bad. He was chief of a band of white-eyes so wicked that everyone feared them. This Gal-lan-tin determined to become rich by killing Apaches and taking their scalps to El Gobernador; but collecting the scalps of Apaches is not either a safe or easy pastime.

"We drove Gal-lan-tin and his band from our country, but later we learned that he was collecting much money for 'Apache' scalps. Then we heard that we had been raiding the villages of the Papago, the Opatah and the Yaqui, killing many, and that we had entered Mexico upon the war trail and killed many Mexicans. All this time we had been in our own country, not having made a raid into Mexico, or upon any other Indian tribes. We were not at war. We were at peace.

"After a while Gal-lan-tin and his band were caught by Mexican troops in the act of scalping some Mexicans they had killed, and then everyone knew, what the Apaches had known for a long time, that it was Gal-lan-tin who had killed the Papagos, the Opatahs, the Yaquis and the Mexicans; and we laughed in our blankets when we thought of El Gobernador del Chihuahua paying out good silver for the scalps of his neighbors and his friends.

"Thus, by accident, was the truth learned in this case; but there were many other murders committed by white-eyes and Mexicans that were blamed upon the Apaches. That is the way of the pindah lickoyee. They are fools. They find a dead man and they say he was killed by Apaches. The Apaches find a dead man and they can read all about him the story of his death. They do not have to guess. Not so the pindah lickoyee."

"What became of Gal-lan-tin?" inquired Shoz-Dijiji.

"He escaped from the Mexican soldiers and brought his band to New Mexico. There they bought some sheep and stole more than nab-kee-go-nay-nan-too-ooh, making in all some twenty-five hundred head, and with these they started for the country which the pindah lickoyee call California.

"On the shores of a great river which separates that country from ours the Yuma Indians fell upon them and killed them all. The

69

Apaches were sorry that it had not fallen to their lot to kill Gal-lan-tin and his band, for they had many sheep."

Shortly after daylight the Apaches camped while Geronimo, Shoz-Dijiji and one other watched the trail behind. The Indians made no fire lest pursuers might be attracted by the smoke. A few held the herd in a grassy canyon while the others slept. Far to the south of them Geronimo and the warrior dozed in the shade of a stunted cedar on a hillside while Shoz-Dijiji watched with untiring eyes the rearward trail.

Having eaten, Shoz-Dijiji quenched his thirst from his water bottle, drawing the liquid into his mouth through his drinking reed, a bit of cane, attached to his scanty apparel by a length of buckskin, for no water might touch his lips during his four novitiate excursions upon the war trail. Treasured therefore was his sacred drinking reed without which he must choose between death by thirst and the loss of credit for all that he had performed upon the war trail, together with the attendant ridicule of the tribe.

Only slightly less esteemed was another treasure dangling from a second buckskin thong—a bit of cedar three inches in length and less than half an inch in width. This was his scratch stick, an article that he found constant use for, since he might not scratch himself with his fingers during this holy period of initiation into the rites and mysteries of the sacred war trail. These two necessary adjuncts to the successful consummation of his ambition he had fashioned in the high places under the eyes of Usen; he had sanctified them with prayer and the sacrificial offering of hoddentin and he had brought them to Nakay-do-klunni, the great izze nantan, to be blessed, and so he set great store by them, but he was glad that soon he would not have to carry them upon the war trail.

With one more test of his fitness, which might come this very day or the next, he would be ready to go before the council prepared to lay away forever the last vestiges of his youth; and so he strained his eyes in an effort to discover the first signs of pursuit which might afford him the opportunity he craved.

A warrior! The young blood surged hot and savage in his veins, conjured by that magic word. A warrior! To come and go as he wished, master of his own destiny, answerable to none; his achievements limited only by the measure of his own prowess. He saw himself a great chief—war chief of all the Apaches. And in the vivid picture that imagination projected upon his screen of dreams the same figures, the same scenes recurred interminably; the war trail, where he fought the blue-clad soldiers of the pindah lickoyee side by side with his best friend, Gian-nah-tah; the council, with the sinister figure of Juh thwarted, confounded at every turn and finally

70

locked with Shoz-Dijiji in a duel to death; the camp, where in his own tepee he rested after the war trail and the chase in the arms of Ish-kay-nay.

Geronimo awoke and relieving the youth told him to sleep. The day wore on, the three relieving one another in turn. Shoz-Dijiji had led the three horses to a tiny spring to water them and to fill the water bottles of his companions and his own. Geronimo was watching—back toward the south.

Throw yourself prone beside this savage sentinel and follow his gaze along the back trail. Your eyes just top the summit of a ridge which hides your body from an enemy approaching from the south. A small bush, from which you have broken a few branches that you may have an unobstructed field of vision, masks that portion of your head that rises above the ridge. An enemy might approach you up the southern slope of the ridge to within a few feet of the concealing bush and not detect your presence.

Just below, to the south, is a tiny meadow, its grasses sere and yellow; for the rains passed months ago. Beneath a single tree at the upper end of the meadow is a mud hole where Shoz-Dijiji, having filled the water bottles, is letting the ponies drink. Farther on the canyon widens where it debouches on a rolling plain that stretches on and on to hazy mountains in the south. There are mountains to the west, too; and close at hand, in the east, rise the more imposing Sierra Madre.

The plain shimmers in the heat that is still intense, though the sun is low. The sage and the greasewood point long, shadowy fingers toward the Mother of Mountains. Nowhere in all that vast expanse that your eye can see is there a sign of life. You might be looking upon a dead world or a painted canvas. The slow lengthening of the shadows is imperceptible. You see nothing that might even remotely suggest life, beyond the solitary brave watering the ponies below you; but that is because the asthenia of civilization has left you half blind as well as half deaf, for where you see nothing and hear nothing Geronimo is conscious of life, movement and sound—of rodents, reptiles and birds awaiting, quiescent, the lessening heat of dusk.

Of these things he is merely conscious, his attention being centered upon some tiny specks moving in the haze of the distant horizon. These you could not see if they were pointed out, much less recognize; but Geronimo has been watching them for some time. He has recognized them, counted them. He half turned toward his companion who was freshening the paint upon his face.

"The vaqueros are coming after their ponies," he said. "There are nine of them."

71

The other crawled to his side and looked. "They will camp here tonight," he said. "It is the first water."

Geronimo nodded and grunted some brief instructions. The warrior made his way leisurely down to the water hole, which Shoz-Dijiji had now left. Arrived at his destination he proceeded to carry out the instructions of his chief, muddying the water hole and then befouling it beyond use by man or beast. Disgusting? Hideous? Cruel? Do not forget that he was on the war trail. Do not forget that he was only a savage, primitive Apache Indian. Make allowances for him. Had he had the cultural advantages of the gorgeous generals of civilization he might have found the means to unloose a poison gas that would have destroyed half the population of Sonora.

For two hours the three Be-don-ko-hes watched the approaching Mexicans. Then Geronimo told the warrior to take three ponies and go northward along the trail of the herd for a mile or two, awaiting there the coming of him and Shoz-Dijiji.

It was nine o'clock before the nine vaqueros, tired, hot, dusty, thirsty, threw themselves from their saddles in the little meadow and sought the water hole. Presently there arose upon the still night air lurid profanity. Above, looking down upon the starlit scene, the two watchers grinned while the vaqueros held council. Should they press on or should they remain here in a dry camp for the night?

Their horses were jaded. It was ten miles to the next water; but most serious of all, they might overtake the Apaches in the dark defiles of the mountains, and they did not want the Apaches to know that they were following until they found a place where they might strike with greater likelihood of success. To be discovered by the enemy now, at night, would be to court extermination. They decided to remain where they were until dawn, and so they left one man on guard while the others slept. Just above them lay the war chief of all the Apaches with his son, Shoz-Dijiji, watching their every move.

An hour passed. The tethered horses of the Mexicans, jaded, stood with drooping heads. The camp slept, even to the single sentry. He was but a youth—a very tired youth—who had fought manfully against sleep until it had become torture. Then he had succumbed.

Geronimo whispered to Shoz-Dijiji and the young brave slipped silently over the summit of the ridge and wormed his way down toward the sleeping bivouac. With the caution of a panther moving upon its prey he crept. No loosened stone, no complaining twig, no rustling grasses bespoke his passing. The shadow of a floating cloud had been as audible. Above him, his Springfield cocked and ready, Geronimo covered the youth's advance, but there was no need.

Shoz-Dijiji went quietly to the horses, calming them with soothing, whispered words. Quickly he cut both ends of the picket line to which they were tethered, and grasping one loose end in his hand moved slowly up the canyon, the horses following him. Half a mile from the camp Geronimo joined him. Behind them the vaqueros slept on undisturbed, their lives preserved by the grim humor of the Apache war chief.

Geronimo was pleased. He derived immense satisfaction by picturing the astonishment and chagrin of the Mexicans when they awoke in the morning and found themselves afoot many weary, waterless miles from the nearest rancho. He visualized their surprise when they realized that Apaches had been in their camp while they slept; and he guessed that they would not loiter on the trail toward the south, for he justly appraised, and gloried in, the fear that that name aroused in the hearts of his enemies.

Presently Geronimo voiced the call of the owl and faintly from afar he heard it answered ahead of them, and knew that their companion was awaiting there with their ponies.

At noon the next day they overtook their fellows and turned the newly captured stock in with the balance of the herd. With great gusto they recounted their exploit. That is, Geronimo and the warrior did. The ban of silence kept Shoz-Dijiji's tongue still in his head, but it did not prevent him strutting just ever so little.

IX

LOVE

THERE was rejoicing in the camp of the Be-don-ko-he when the war party returned with its spoil. Victorio and Juh were there with a hunting party of Chi-hen-ne and Ned-ni and they joined in the jubilation, the feasting and the drinking and in the council of the warriors that was held in the open, the braves sitting in a circle about a small fire while Geronimo, eloquent with tizwin, narrated the exploits of his party, his style fettered by no embarrassing restraint of modesty.

To Shoz-Dijiji he gave full credit for the stealing of the horses of the Mexicans, pointing out that while no fight ensued this exploit was fully as much to the youth's credit as any engagement with arms, since it required craft, cunning and bravery of a high order. He expatiated upon Shoz-Dijiji's strength and courage in his duel with the mounted vaquero, and in his peroration called upon the council to vote Shoz-Dijiji's admission to the warrior class.

When he had sat down others arose and spoke of the valor of the candidate, of his prowess upon the war trail, his skill and tirelessness in the chase, of his exemplary conduct during his novitiate. Victorio spoke for him and many another noted warrior, and then Juh arose, sullen, scowling.

"Chiefs and warriors of the Shis-Inday," he said, "a warrior is known not alone by the things that he does but by those that he fails to do. The names of Delgadito, Mangas Colorado, Cochise, Victorio, Geronimo and Juh strike terror to the hearts of their foes.

"The enemy is filled with fear and ready to retreat at the mention of these names. Why? Because all these warriors made death or capture so horrible that the hearts of all their enemies turn to water before a weapon is raised in combat. Upon this fact more than upon their bravery and skill rests their great value to the Shis-Inday.

"One who is afraid to torture is a coward and unfitted to be a warrior. Such is Shoz-Dijiji. His heart is as soft as a woman's breast. To most of us Shoz-Dijiji is known best by his continued refusal to torture. Even as a child he joined not with the other children in torturing the birds and animals which they snared, and never once upon the war trail has he inflicted pain upon a wounded or prisoner enemy. I, Juh, will not vote to make Shoz-Dijiji a warrior."

After he had resumed his seat there was silence around the council fire for several minutes. Then Geronimo arose. In his heart was murder, but in his cruel features, schooled to obey his will, there was no hint of it.

"Juh, Chief of the Ned-ni, knows that a single voice raised against Shoz-Dijiji now will prevent him from being admitted to the warrior class until he has undergone another trial upon the war trail. Geronimo knows that the words of Juh are not prompted by loyalty to the Shis-Inday as much as they are by hatred of Shoz-Dijiji. This is not the act of a brave warrior or a great chief. Such things bring strife among the Shis-Inday. Does Juh wish to change his words before it is too late?"

The chief of the Ned-ni sprang to his feet. "Juh has spoken," he cried. "Juh does not change his words. Let Shoz-Dijiji change his ways to the ways of a warrior and Juh will, perhaps, speak differently at another council."

"The laws of the Shis-Inday were made by Usen," said Geronimo, "and they may not be lightly changed. The words have been spoken and not recalled. Shoz-Dijiji must go again upon the war trail and prove himself once again fit to become a warrior. I, Geronimo, war chief of the Apaches say these words." He sat down.

However keen the disappointment of Shoz-Dijiji when he was told of the action of the council, he received the information with the stolid indifference of an Indian, though within his breast the fires of his hatred for Juh burned with renewed fury. Ish-kay-nay, understanding, spoke words of praise and comfort, and Gian-rah-tah applied vile, obscene Apache epithets to the great chief Juh—when he was sure that no Ned-ni might overhear him.

Ish-kay-nay had a suggestion to make. "Upon the next raid, Shoz-Dijiji," she advised, "do not kill. Torture the living, mutilate the dead. Show them that your heart is strong."

"Never!" exclaimed Shoz-Dijiji. "If for no other reason, because Juh wishes me to, I will not do it."

"Why do you not torture?" asked Ish-kay-nay. "You are brave—everyone knows that—so it cannot be that you are afraid."

"I see no sense in it," replied the young brave. "It gives me no pleasure." He paused. "Ish-kay-nay, l cannot explain why it is and I have never told any one before, but when I see warriors torturing the helpless wounded and the defenseless prisoner, mutilating dead men who have fought bravely, something comes into my heart which is not pride of my people. I am ashamed, Ish-kay-nay, of even my own father, Geronimo.

"I do not know why. I only know that I speak true words without understanding them. I know that I am no coward; but I should not be so sure of that had I plunged a red hot king bolt into a screaming white woman, as I have seen Juh do, and laughed at her agonies of death."

"If you feel pity for the enemy you are weak," said Ish-kay-nay, sternly.

"I do not feel pity," replied Shoz-Dijiji. "I care not how much they suffer. I only know that it gives me no pleasure to watch them and that I do not think that it shows bravery to raise a weapon against any creature which cannot inflict harm upon you in return, except in the chase, where any man may kill for food."

"Perhaps Shoz-Dijiji is right," said Ish-kay-nay "I had never thought of it in this way before."

"I know I am right, and I shall not torture if I never become a warrior!"

But he had not a great while to wait before his chance came. Living, as the Apache did, in constant danger of attack by the soldiers of two civilized powers as well as by raiding parties of hostile Indian tribes, he found it expedient, in the interest of survival, to maintain constant, unflagging watchfulness. To this end Geronimo, however safely he might consider his village hidden, kept scouts almost constantly in the field.

To this duty, one in which he delighted, Shoz-Dijiji was often detailed. It sent him alone into the solitudes that he loved, to play in stern reality the games of his childhood. It kept him always hard and fit for the war trail—the ultimate hope and ambition of the warrior. It practiced him continually in the wood and plain craft in which he already excelled.

Sometimes, astride Nejeunee, he covered prodigious distances in a day, but oftener, on foot, he also covered prodigious distances. Forty, fifty, at times a hundred miles of barren land would unroll beneath his steady jog in a single day. His great lungs pushed out his giant chest. The muscles of his mighty legs might, it almost seemed, turn a bullet, so hard were they. He was a man now, by the standards of the Apache, except for the fact that he had not yet been admitted to the warrior class.

Among the Be-don-ko-he he was looked upon with respect and admiration, for they knew that it was only the hatred of Juh that prevented him from being a warrior. Upon the war trail and in the chase he had proved himself all that a warrior should be, and he carried himself with the restraint and dignity of a chief. Ish-kay-nay was very proud of him, for it was no secret in the tribe that when Shoz-Dijiji became a warrior his pony would be tied before her tepee, nor was there one who believed that she would wait the full four days before leading it to water and feeding it.

Afoot, fifty miles from camp, Shoz-Dijiji was scouting. A few miles ahead in the hills there was water and toward this he was making his way one mid-afternoon. A blistering sun poured down upon him, the superheated earth and rocks of the trail gave it back in searing intensity. The country he had crossed had been entirely waterless, and so it was that Shoz-Dijiji looked forward to the little spring hidden in these seemingly arid hills, a spring known only to his people, sacred to the Apaches.

Suddenly there was wafted to the Indian's nostrils the faintest suggestion of an acrid odor and simultaneously he vanished from the landscape, so quickly did he react to this tenuous hint of danger. A greasewood hid him from the direction down which a barely moving current of air had wafted this certain indication of the presence of man. From straight ahead it came, from the direction in which he was going. Where there was smoke there was man and man would not be making a fire in this vicinity elsewhere than beside the water where Shoz-Dijiji was planning to quench his thirst.

From beneath the greasewood his keen eyes looked out toward the low hill behind which lay the water, and now he saw thin smoke arising. So little was the smoke that Shoz-Dijiji almost felt that it had been made by Indians, yet, too, he knew that near the water there was little wherewith to make a fire, and so, perchance, the pindah lickoyee, who ordinarily make great fires, foolishly, had been forced to make a small fire from want of fuel. Therefore he could not be sure whether Indians or whites were concealed behind that little hill. If they were the former, and Apaches, well and good, but if they were not, then they were enemies, for every man's hand is against the Apache.

Shoz-Dijiji, with the patience that is only an Indian's, lay silent, motionless for hours. As he lay he broke branches from the greasewood, which chanced to be an unusually large bush, until at last he had gathered enough to form quite a respectable screen. Then, having seen or heard no further signs of life from beyond the hill, he crawled forward a few inches, keeping the screen before him. Again he lay motionless for a while, watching, before he advanced a short distance.

This he kept up for a full hour, during which he had covered the distance to the foot of the hill and up its slope almost to the summit. Now he could hear voices, and they told him that he was approaching the camp of white men—three of them.

Shoz-Dijiji felt the heat of just anger surge through him. What

77

right had these aliens at the water hole of the Shis-Inday? For a thousand thousand years had this spring been hidden away from the sight of man, just where Usen had placed it for the use of the six tribes. That three white-eyed men should camp beside it, quench their thirst, cook their food, sleep and move on, aroused, of itself, no resentment in the heart of Shoz-Dijiji; it was the foregone conclusion of the aftermath that caused his apprehension and his determination to prevent the natural sequences of this event.

He and his people had seen the pindah lickoyee "discover" their hidden springs and water holes many times before in the past. In ones or twos or threes the white-eyed men had stumbled upon these gifts of Usen to his people in the arid places, and presently a trail was beaten to them and many of the white-eyed ones came, and the birds and the game were frightened away. Often a fence was built around the water and a white man with bushy whiskers, and dirt in his ears, guarded it, a rifle in one hand, a bottle of whiskey in the other, making other white men pay for the water, keeping the Indians away from it entirely.

Warriors of the Be-don-ko-he, fathers of his playmates, had been shot by such men when they had sought to quench their thirst at springs from which they had drunk since childhood, and that their fathers had used before them beyond the memory of man. Such were the thoughts that filled the heart of Shoz-Dijiji as he crept toward the summit of the hill that hid the usurpers from his view.

At last his eyes looked down upon the scene beyond, burning pits of hate in which there lived no slightest spark of aught but loathing and contempt. The Comanche, the Navajo, the bear, the snake might awaken admiration in the breast of the Apache, but the white man, never!

He saw three bearded men sprawled upon the ground. One of them was frying bacon above a small fire. Two burros, thin, dejected, stood with drooping heads. A third was stretched upon the ground, exhausted. Their packs lay in disorder all about. The men appeared to be weak. Shoz-Dijiji read their story at a glance.

Lost in this waterless wasteland, they had found the spring by accident just in time to save themselves from death. He noted their sunken cheeks and eyes; he saw their feeble movements. But there was no answering pity in his heart. In his mind, however, there arose vividly the recollection of a white soldier wantonly hurling him to the ground, and of his words, the meaning of which he had learned at San Carlos: "What the hell are you doing here, you dirty Siwash?" A shudder ran through the frame of Shoz-Dijiji then, as it always did at recollection of the humiliation of that moment at Hot Springs.

He noted carefully every detail of the scene below him. He saw that the men, with scarce the strength to carry their own weight, had transferred everything to the packs of the burros, even including their rifles and revolvers, and these lay now at a little distance from them, entangled in the piles of carelessly down-thrown tools, bedding and provisions that go to make up the outfits of prospectors.

Shoz-Dijiji withdrew three arrows from his quiver and placed them between his fingers, he grasped his bow and arose to his full height. Silently, majestically he strode down toward the white men. He was almost upon them before he who was watching the bacon discovered him. The others had been lying with closed eyes. The white man gave a cry of alarm, that cry that had sent the chill of fear along countless white spines for three hundred years "Apaches!" and staggered weakly in an effort to reach his rifle.

"What the hell are you doing here, you dirty white-eyes?" demanded Shoz-Dijiji in English; but he did not wait for a reply— the soldier who had thrown him to the ground at Hot Springs had not and he had learned his technique from the white soldier. Instead, his bow string twanged and an iron-shod arrow pierced the heart of the prospector. The two remaining whites sprang to defend themselves, one seizing a hand axe, the other the hot frying pan, the only weapons within their reach. With swift rapidity two more arrows leaped from the mesquite bow.

With the hand axe Shoz-Dijiji made assurance of death doubly sure, then he scalped the three, selected from their persons and their packs everything that could prove of value to an Apache, packed the loot upon the two stronger burros, quenched his thirst and, leading the animals, moved on into the hills for about two miles. Here he cached in a small cave everything but a single rifle, a six-shooter and a belt of ammunition, which he appropriated to his own immediate use, turned the burros loose and started back toward the camp of his people, fifty miles away.

Travelling in the lesser heat of the night, taking short cuts across open valleys that he must avoid in the light of day, Shoz-Dijiji made rapid progress, arriving in camp about two o'clock the following morning, some eight hours after he had left his loot cached in the mountains.

When he awoke, well after midday, he exhibited his newly acquired arms, boasted of his exploit, and showed the three bloody scalps as proof of his prowess.

"I, myself, Shoz-Dijiji," he said, "crept alone upon the camp of the pindah lickoyee. There were three of them, but Shoz-Dijiji knows not the word fear. In the broad light of chigo-na-ay he walked down into the camp of the white-eyes and slew them. He took much loot and hid it in a cave in the mountains. Here are the scalp locks of the white-eyed men. Here are the weapons of one of them."

Geronimo grunted approvingly. Victorio fingered the rifle of the dead prospector enviously. Juh was not there. With his Ned-ni he had returned to his own country. To Shoz-Dijiji came an inspiration.

"There are two more rifles in the cave in the mountains," he said; "one for Geronimo and one for Victorio, and there are presents for many braves and their women. If Geronimo speaks the words Shoz-Dijiji will return with ponies and fetch these things for his friends."

Geronimo nodded. "Go," he said, "and take Gian-nah-tah with you. He can help." So that very night Shoz-Dijiji and Gian-nah-tah set out upon their ponies with two led animals upon which to pack the loot; and Geronimo said to Victorio: "Shoz-Dijiji took the war trail and slew three of the enemies of his people. If he returns with loot he has proved that he is fit to be a warrior. We will hold a council and vote again."

"Yes," agreed Victorio, "if he returns with many presents we will make him a warrior. Juh is not here."

Three days later Shoz-Dijiji and Gian-nah-tah returned. The former turned over all the loot, except one rifle, a revolver and ammunition for himself, to Geronimo to distribute, announcing that he was going that very night to the high places to pray to Usen, to make big medicine and to prepare himself to become a warrior. His words and manner carried a definite inference that he fully expected to be admitted to the council of warriors before he returned. Geronimo laid his hand upon the shoulder of his son and there were both pride and affection in the gesture.

"When Shoz-Dijiji returns from the high places," he said, "he will be a warrior, or there will be a new chief of the Be-don-ko-he, for Geronimo will be dead."

But Geronimo did not die, and when Shoz-Dijiji returned after two days of prayer he found himself a warrior. The first great ambition of his life was achieved and now the road lay clear to any heights to which he might aspire. He was his own master, free to go and come as inclination prompted.

He could take a squaw, or as many of them as he could afford. Though he had but three ponies, which were scarcely enough to compensate any fond father for the loss of the least attractive of daughters, he was in no way down-hearted. The girl of his choice would unquestionably command several times three ponies, but

Shoz-Dijiji knew that he would win her and he was happy. He had no thought in his heart for any other mate. Ish-kay-nay would never have a rival in the affections of Shoz-Dijiji. Unquestionably he would take other squaws as the years passed, thus lightening the domestic burdens of Ish-kay-nay, since nothing less could be expected of an important and prosperous warrior who had a name and dignity to uphold. Ish-kay-nay would expect at least this much consideration, and she would be ashamed if he proved too poor a provider or too penurious a mate to support an establishment commensurate with the social standing of her family and his; but that would come later—at first they would be alone.

Shoz-Dijiji had not seen Ish-kay-nay alone for a long time, but tonight he found her and together they wandered into the forest and sat upon the bole of a fallen tree. He held one of her hands in his and putting an arm about her slim, young shoulders he drew her to him. "My father is very angry," confided Ish-kay-nay.

"Why?" asked Shoz-Dijiji.

"Because I did not feed and water the pony of Juh, chief of the Ned-ni."

"You do not love Juh," stated Shoz-Dijiji emphatically.

"I love only Shoz-Dijiji," whispered the girl, snuggling closer to the bronze chest. "But the father of Ish-kay-nay knowing that Juh is a powerful chief thinks that it would be best for him if his daughter belonged to Juh.

"He speaks often to me about it and he grows angry when I refuse. Juh came last time to our village to make talk to my father of this matter. My father talked to me, but still I would not listen. When he told him, Juh was very angry and said that he knew who I was waiting for, but that I would wait forever as he would see that Shoz-Dijiji never became a warrior.

"Of course such talk is foolish talk and my father knew it and that sooner or later you must become a warrior, for he is not blind to the fact that you are already mighty upon the war trail and a great hunter; but he sought to find another way to discourage Ish-kay-nay. He said that he would demand so many ponies from you that you would be an old man before you could gather them, and that unless I wanted a warrior before it was too late I had better let him send for Juh again."

"I will get the ponies," said Shoz-Dijiji.

"If you cannot, I will run away with you," said Ish-kay-nay.

Shoz-Dijiji shook his head. "I do not have to run away with my squaw," he said proudly. "I will take her before all men and give her father as many ponies as he demands."

"If it takes a long time Ish-kay-nay will wait," announced the

81

girl, simply. Then, as though moved by a disturbing reflection, "But what if Ish-kay-nay waits so long that she is old and wrinkled? Then Shoz-Dijiji will not want her."

The young brave laughed and pressed her closer. "Shoz-Dijiji will always want Ish-kay-nay," he insisted, "even though she be as wrinkled and old as Tze-go-juni, the medicine woman of the Cho-kon-en; but Ish-kay-nay will not have to wait so long as that, for tomorrow morning she will find Nejeunee tied before her tepee.

"Poor Nejeunee! Always has he been fed and watered promptly when he was not running free upon the range. He will be sad when he sees chigo-na-ay rise and set four times while he stands thirsting for water and hungering for good grama grass." He bent and looked quizzically into the girl's face, half revealed by the rays of klego-na-ay filtering softly silver through the spreading branches of the pines.

Ish-kay-nay looked up and smiled. "Nejeunee shall be fed and watered at dawn," she told him.

"No," he said, "Ish-kay-nay must wait at least two days, lest the girls and the women make fun of her and think her immodest, or too anxious to have a warrior."

The girl threw her head up haughtily. "No one will dare say that of Ish-kay-nay," she cried fiercely. "Nor will anyone think it. Does not every one know that I can have Juh, or any of a dozen of the bravest warriors of the Be-don-ko-he, Cho-kon-en, the Ned-ni or the Chi-hen-ne? Is it any secret that Shoz-Dijiji loves me, or that I love Shoz-Dijiji? Such foolishness is for fools."

"Ish-kay-nay will be the mother of war chiefs," said Shoz-Dijiji proudly.

"And Shoz-Dijiji will be their father," replied the girl.

X

WICHITA BILLINGS

WHEN morning dawned it did not find Nejeunee tied before the tepee of Ish-kay-nay, for the pinto stallion was far away upon the war trail with his savage master. Word had come to Geronimo, even while Shoz-Dijiji and Ish-kay-nay were making love in the woods, that troops from San Carlos were looking for him, the bodies of the three prospectors having been discovered by two Navajo scouts in the employ of the government.

Immediately the peaceful camp of the Be-don-ko-he became the scene of hurried preparation for flight and for the war trail. A scouting party of a dozen braves was dispatched in the direction from which the troops might be expected, to watch and report their movements; if necessary, to hold them in check while the main body of the Be-don-ko-he, with their women, their children, their pony herd and their camp equipment made good their escape across the line into Mexico.

Hurriedly were war bands adjusted, grim faces streaked with pigment, weapons looked to, ponies caught and bridled. For the first time as a warrior Shoz-Dijiji prepared for the war trail. Across his swart face, from ear to ear, he painted a broad band of vermilion, laying on the pigment boldly with the index finger of his right hand, stooping low toward the light of a little fire, his features reflected in a small round mirror held in his left hand. Above and below the vermilion band he laid a coat of blue, the base of which was a ground micaceous stone. A single necklace adorned his throat and two small silver rings were in his ears.

Attached to his person and concealed from view was his tzi-daltai, wrapped in a three-inch square of buckskin upon which were painted crooked lines of red and yellow, depicting the red snake and the yellow. This phylactery was in itself big medicine and very sacred; it added to the potency of his tzi-daltai, rendering that amulet all powerful. In addition to the tzi-daltai the phylactery contained a bit of sacred turquoise, and a tiny cross of lightning riven pine, which Shoz-Dijiji called intchi-dijin, the black wind. Upon these things no alien eye might look without destroying their efficacy. For this reason the little package was securely hidden in the folds of his loin cloth.

Upon his legs Shoz-Dijiji drew his long war moccasins with their rawhide soles and protecting toe armor, their tops, three feet long, he turned down from just below the knee, thus still further protecting the lower leg from the sharp spines of the cactus. Slender thongs of buckskin, leading from the moccasin tops to the belt of his loin cloth, kept the former from falling down around his ankles. A pair of cotton drawers encased his legs and a quiet-hued print shirt covered his torso, its skirts falling outside the drawers. There was a cartridge belt around his waist and a six-shooter and a butcher knife at his hips, but he also carried his beloved bow and arrows as well as the rifle he had taken from the white prospector.

Shoz-Dijiji preferred the nakedness of a single loin cloth, for thus it had been his wont to go in all weathers since he wore anything at all, but custom seemed to demand these other things of full fledged warriors, though all were accustomed to discard them upon the eve of battle, and as he had just attained the status of the warrior class he felt it incumbent upon him to uphold its traditions even to the point making himself supremely uncomfortable in hated shirt and drawers. However, the party had been upon the trail but a short time before he discovered that the drawers wrinkled and chafed him and they were discarded with no regrets; and later in the day he removed his shirt and gave it to Gian-nah-tah.

"It makes me look like a pindah lickoyee," he confided to his friend. "In it I do not feel free. I shall not wear it."

His bronzed hide, naked to the elements almost from birth, little felt the hot rays of the sun, thus eliminating the only practical reason why an Apache should wear a shirt at all. Thus Shoz-Dijiji rode almost naked—except for moccasins, G-string and head bandanna he was quite naked. Beneath his bandanna he wore the war band about his brow confining his black hair, slicked smooth with tallow. It was not long after the shirt went that he removed the bandanna, breathing a sigh of relief, for now Shoz-Dijiji was himself again.

Before dawn the party had separated, the braves, in pairs, moving at right angles to their original line of march, and in both directions, forming at last a thin line of scouts that surveyed from hidden vantage spots a front of sixty miles extending east and west across the lines the troops would naturally follow as they marched down from San Carlos.

Signals had been arranged and the rendezvous designated by the sub-chief in command. The braves were to proceed as quickly as possible to certain advantageous positions indicated by the sub-chief. There they were to remain until they sighted troops, or received the signal that other scouts had sighted them. They were to stay concealed and, if possible, avoid battle.

Shoz-Dijiji was accompanied by Gian-na-tah, and together they rode through the night toward their appointed station, which they reached shortly after dawn, making a slight detour to avoid a ranch house, and coming at last to the rocky rim of a canyon through which led a well-travelled road along which it was a foregone conclusion that troops would pass if they followed a certain route to the border.

In lieu of a saddle Shoz-Dijiji rode astride a well-worn gray blanket. This he removed from Nejeunee's back after they had hidden the two ponies in a narrow ravine a mile from the road. Coming to the rim of the canyon, Shoz-Dijiji lay flat upon his belly, his head at the very edge of the summit of the precipitous wall of the canyon. Quickly Gian-nah-tah draped the gray blanket about the black poll of his friend, sprinkled dirt about its edges where they met the ground, leaving only a small opening through which the keen eyes of the Black Bear might take in the whole of the canyon below.

From the road the most suspicious might have looked carefully and seen only another gray boulder upon the canyon's rim. Gian-nah-tah, entirely concealed from the sight of anyone passing through the canyon, watched northward along the flank, where a careful and experienced Indian fighter would send Indian scouts before permitting his command to enter the narrow canyon, so eminently suited to sudden and disastrous ambush. He also watched to east and west for the signal that would announce the discovery of the enemy by another scout.

Patience is a quality of mind and will but vaguely sensed by civilized races. The higher types of savages have it developed to a degree of outstanding virtue but perhaps, of all peoples, the North American Indians have achieved it most closely to perfection, and of these it remained for the Apaches to raise it to the pinnacle of highest specialization. With Shoz-Dijiji as with his fellows it was a fine art in which he took just pride.

Thus it was that for hours he could lie perfectly motionless, watching the silent, deserted, dusty road below. No sound escaped his ears, no odor, his nostrils; his eyes saw everything within the range of their vision. No lizard moved, no insect crawled along its way that Shoz-Dijiji did not see and note. A rattle-snake crossed the road and disappeared among the rocks upon the other side; a horned toad, basking in the sun, awaiting unwary flies, attracted his attention by its breathing so quiet and still were the surroundings that even the gentle rising and falling of its warty hide attracted the quick eyes of the Apache; a darting swift was as sure of detection as would an Indian elephant have been.

And as he lay there his mind was occupied with many thoughts, mostly somber, for the mind of the Apache inclines in that direction. This background, however, was often shot with lights of a happier vein—with recollections of Ish-kay-nay and anticipations. He considered, pridefully, the traditions of his people, the glory of their past, the exploits of their greatest warriors; he pondered the wrongs that had been inflicted upon them by their enemies.

He recalled the tales of the murders committed upon them by Mexicans and whites—the differentiation of color is strictly and solely Apache—he reviewed the numerous and increasing thefts of their ancestral lands. These thoughts awakened within him no self-pity as they might have in an Anglo-Saxon, so thoroughly had training and environment succeeded in almost erasing hereditary inclinations; instead they aroused hatred and a desire for vengeance.

His thoughts, gloomy or roseate, were suddenly interrupted by a faint sound that came down out of the north. It grew in intensity, so that Shoz-Dijiji knew that whatever caused it was approaching, and he knew what was causing it, the feet of horses moving at a walk. Listening, he determined that they were too few to announce the approach of a body of troops. Perhaps a few scouts rode in advance. He waited, watching the northern end of the canyon.

Presently three bearded men rode into view. They were not soldiers. They were not cowboys. Shoz-Dijiji identified them as of that class of fools who scratched around in arid hills for the yellow iron, pesh-litzogue. He gazed down upon them with contempt. His fingers, resting upon his rifle, twitched. What a wonderful target they presented! But he was scouting and must forego this Usen-given opportunity. Of course the sub-chief had only mentioned specifically the soldiers of the white-eyes, when he had warned them against engaging the enemy. Technically Shoz-Dijiji would be committing no disobedience were he to rid the world of these three quite useless creatures; but he knew that he had been sent here to watch for soldiers and for nothing else, so he curbed his desire.

The floor of the canyon was dotted with boulders, large and small, among which the road wound. Some of the boulders were larger than a large tepee, offering splendid cover. Behind them more than one man had fought and died, making his last stand.

Shoz-Dijiji was suddenly attracted by a sound coming from the south, a rhythmical sound that announced the approach of a loping horse. Two of the three men drew quickly behind a great boulder, the third behind another on the opposite side of the road. The

Apache waited, watching. The loping horse drew nearer. He entered the lower end of the canyon and presently came within the range of Shoz-Dijiji's vision. Its rider was a girl—a white girl.

Even from where he lay he saw that she was very good to look at. As she came abreast of the three whites they rode directly into the road and barred her passage, and as she sought to wheel her horse one of them reached out and seized her bridle rein. The girl reached for a six-shooter that hung at her hip, a cold, blue Colt; but another of the three had slipped from his saddle and run to her side. Now he grasped her wrist, tore the weapon from its holster and dragged the girl to the ground. It was all done very quickly. Shoz-Dijiji watched. His hatred for the men mounted.

He could hear the words that were spoken below and he understood them. He heard the girl call one of the men by name, demanding that they release her. He felt the contempt in her tone and a like sentiment for them in his own breast aroused within him, unconsciously, a sense of comradeship with the girl.

"Your old man kicked me out," growled the man she had addressed. "You told him to. I wasn't good enough for you, eh? You'll find I am. You're goin' with me, but you ain't a-goin' as Mrs. Cheetim—you're goin' as Dirty Cheetim's woman. Sabe?"

The girl seemed very cool. Shoz-Dijiji could not but admire her. The ethics of the proceedings did not interest him; but suddenly he became aware of the fact that his interest was keenly aroused and that his inclinations were strongly upon the side of the girl. He did not know why. He did not attempt to analyze his feelings. He only knew that it pleased him to interfere.

He heard the girl's reply. Her voice was steady, level, low. It had a quality that touched hidden chords within the breast of the Apache, arousing pleasant reactions.

"You are a fool, Cheetim," she said. "You know my old man. He will kill you if he has to follow you to Hell to get you, and you know it."

"They'll be two of us in Hell then," replied Cheetim. "Come on— git back on that cayuse." He jerked her roughly. The barrel of a rifle slid quietly from beneath the edge of a gray boulder at the top of the canyon's wall; there was a loud report that rebounded thunderously from wall to wall. Cheetim dropped in his tracks.

"Apaches!" screamed one of the remaining men and scrambled into his saddle, closely followed by his companion. The girl's horse wheeled and ran toward the south. Another shot and one of the fleeing men toppled from his saddle. The girl looked up to see a painted, all but naked warrior leaping down the steep canyon side

87

toward her. She reached for her Colt, forgetting that it was gone. Then he was beside her. She stood there bravely, facing him.

"Nejeunee," announced Shoz-Dijiji, which means friend or friendly; but the girl did not understand. He held out his hand; this she understood. She took it, smiling.

"You sabe English?" she asked.

"No savvy," lied Shoz-Dijiji. He picked up the Colt, where it lay beside the dead Cheetim, and handed it to her.

"What your name?" demanded the girl.

"No savvy," said Shoz-Dijiji.

She pointed a finger at her own breast. "Me, Wichita Billings," she announced, and then she pointed the finger at him, questioningly.

"Huh!" exclaimed the Apache. "Shoz-Dijiji," and he pointed at his own deep chest.

Without a word he turned and left her, walking south toward the end of the canyon. The girl followed because in that direction lay the ranch of her father. When she came in sight of the Apache again he had already caught her horse and was leading it toward her. He handed her the bridle rein, pointed toward the ranch and started at a swinging trot up the side of the canyon. Being a wise girl and having lived in Indian country since she was born, Wichita Billings put spurs to her horse and disappeared around a bend in the canyon toward the squat, fortified ranch house that was her home.

Why the Apache had befriended her she could not guess; but for that matter Shoz-Dijiji could not guess either why he had acted as he had. He knew what Geronimo or Juh would have done. He wondered why he had not done likewise.

Halfway between the ranch and the canyon Wichita Billings met her father and two of his ranch hands. Faintly they had heard the shots from the direction of the canyon and knowing that the girl had ridden in that direction they had started out to investigate. Briefly she told them what had transpired and Billings was frankly puzzled.

"Must have been a reservation Indian on pass," he decided. "Maybe some buck we give grub to some time."

Wichita shook her head. "I never seen him before," she said, "and, Dad, that siwash wasn't on no pass, he was on the warpath— paint, fixin's an' all. He didn't have nothin' on but a G-string an' moccasins, an' he was totin' a young arsenal."

"Ole Geronimo's been out quite some time," said one of the hands; "most likely it was one of his Cheeracows. Wisht I'd a-been there."

"What would you a-done?" inquired the girl, contemptuously.

"They'd a-been one more good Injun," boasted the man.

"Say, if you'd been there they couldn't no one of seen your coat-tails for the dust, Hank," laughed the girl as she gathered her horse and reined toward the ranch again. "Besides I think that buck was one pretty good Indian, alive; the way he took my part against Cheetim."

"They ain't only one kind of a good Injun," grumbled Hank, "an' that's a dead one."

From behind a distant boulder Shoz-Dijiji and Gian-nah-tah watched the four as they rode toward the ranch. "Why did you let the woman go?" asked Gian-nah-tah.

"Gian-nah-tah," said Shoz-Dijiji, "this I may say to you because we are long time friends and because Gian-nah-tah knows that the heart of Shoz-Dijiji is brave: Shoz-Dijiji will never take the war trail against women and children. That is for weaklings and women—not for a great warrior."

Gian-nah-tah shook his head, for he did not understand; nor, for that matter, did Shoz-Dijiji, though each of them pondered the matter carefully for a long time after they had returned to their respective posts.

Gian-nah-tah, following the instructions of Shoz-Dijiji, watched now carefully toward the ranch as well as for smoke signals from the east or west, or for flankers sneaking down through the hills from the north; and at last, far away in the west, a distant smoke rewarded his watching. Faintly at first it arose, a thin gray column against the azure sky, gained in volume, persisted steadily.

Gian-nah-tah crept to Shoz-Dijiji's side, touched him and pointed. The young warrior saw the distant shaft rising unwaveringly through the still, midday air, calling the scattered bands to the rendezvous, sending its message over an area as great as the whole state of West Virginia, to be received with as varied emotions as there were eyes to see it.

It told the savage vedettes where the soldiers of the pindah lickoyee were marching toward the border and where to gather to harass and delay them; it brought an oath to the lips of a grizzled man in dusty blue who rode at the head of a weary, dust-choked column, for it told him that the wily enemy had sighted him and that the clans were gathering to oppose him upon some well-selected field of their own choosing. To the far scattered cowman and miner it cried: "The hostiles are on the war-path!" and set them to barricading ranch house and cabin, oiling breech blocks and counting ammunition; it sent mothers to their knees in prayer, with crying children huddled about them.

It filled the heart of Shoz-Dijiji with joyous song, for it told him

89

that he was soon to fight his first fight as a warrior against the hated warriors of the pindah lickoyee. It urged the main body of the fleeing Be-don-ko-he onward toward the border, torturing, burning, ravishing, killing as it went. For an hour the smoke column hung in the sky, a beacon of the hate, the cruelties, the treacheries, the wrongs that man inflicts on man.

Silently, from east and west, the Be-don-ko-he scouts assembled far to the south of the long dead signal fire; and up from the south came Geronimo the next day with twelve warriors to reinforce them. Slowly they dropped back, leaving sentinels upon their rear and flanks, sentinels who retreated just ahead of the advancing enemy, whose every move was always under observation by a foe he never saw.

The trail narrowed where it entered low, rocky, barren hills. "Hold them here," said Geronimo to a sub-chief, and left four warriors with him, while he retreated another mile into the hills and disposed his men for more determined resistance.

"Hell!" murmured a grizzled man in blue denim overalls down the seams of which the troop tailor had sewn broad yellow stripes. "I don't believe there's an Apache within forty miles of us, outside our own scouts."

A lean, parched sergeant, riding at his side, shook his head. "You can't most always sometimes tell, sir," he volunteered.

From the base of the hills ahead came the crack of a rifle, putting a period to that paragraph. The officer grinned. To the right of the trail was a shallow gully. Into this he led his troop, still in column of fours.

"Prepare to dismount. Dismount! Number twos hold horses! Fall 'em in, sergeant!" He gave commands quietly, coolly. The men obeyed with alacrity. The point, three men riding in advance of the troop, having uncovered the enemy raced back to the shelter of the gully, the bullets of the hostiles pinging about their heads. Far to the rear the pack train and two companies of infantry plodded through the dust.

Behind a rock that barely covered his prone figure from the eyes of the enemy, lay Shoz-Dijiji. Similarly sheltered, four other painted savages fired after the retreating point. One of them was a wrinkled old subchief, a past-master of the art of Apache warfare. The five watched the dismounted cavalrymen deploy into the open, dropping behind bushes and boulders as they wormed their way forward.

There was a burst of fire from the thin line that made the Apaches duck behind their shelter; when they looked again it was to

90

see that the soldiers had advanced, fifty yards, perhaps, and again sought cover. The Indians fired rapidly to give the impression of a larger force than actually constituted this insignificant rear guard. The soldiers peppered away at the puffs of smoke that signaled the positions of the foe.

The sub-chief called across to Shoz-Dijiji and the two wormed themselves back, turned to the left and sought new positions, holding their fire, waiting for the moment the old warrior knew would come. Again the soldiers fired rapidly, half of them concentrating their fire upon the rocks from behind which the puffs of smoke had arisen while the other half arose, and, bent half double, raced forward to new and more advanced positions. It was then that the sub-chief and Shoz-Dijiji opened fire upon them from their new positions that had not yet attracted the fire of the cavalrymen. The grizzled captain saw three of his men stumble forward, their faces in the dirt. Afterward two of them crawled painfully toward cover but the third lay very still.

Angry, the entire troop fired rapidly at the Indian position, until there was no response; then the second half of the troop advanced in a quick rush. From another point, far to the right of that upon which they had been concentrating their fire, came the crack of a rifle and another soldier fell.

Shoz-Dijiji reloaded and fired again. To his rear the sub-chief with the three other warriors was trotting back toward the main body of hostiles that was busily engaged in the construction of simple but effective fortifications under the supervision of Geronimo.

The captain had lost four men and had not seen an Indian. He had no definite idea of the strength of the enemy. He could not advance without exposing his men to the full fire of the hostiles. To his left was a dry wash that afforded complete protection, and into this he ordered his troop, there to await the coming of the infantry. Behind his rock, quite alone, Shoz-Dijiji held off the United States Army while the war chief of all the Apaches prepared for a determined stand a mile to the south.

For an hour the cavalrymen sweltered and cursed in the dusty barranca. Occasionally one would lift a head above the sheltering wall, there would be a crack and the ping of a bullet and the head would duck to safety—Shoz-Dijiji, patient, tireless, eagle-eyed, hung doggedly to his post.

Then the infantry arrived. Out of effective range they took to the barranca, the pack train sheltering in the gully with the horses of the troop. The cavalry, loath to relinquish the honor to doughboys, charged the position of the hostiles after the infantry had poured a steady fusillade of rifle fire into it for several minutes.

Hunched double that they might present the smallest possible target, grasping their carbines at the ready, separated by intervals of a yard or two, the men advanced at the double up the gentle, rock-strewn acclivity. Their grizzled captain led them. A dozen yards beyond the summit he raised his hand and the blue line halted. The officer looked about him. For hundreds of yards in all directions there was not sufficient cover to conceal a cottontail. There was not an Indian in sight.

"Hell!" murmured the captain.

A half mile to the south of him Shoz-Dijiji trotted toward the stronghold of his people, while the blue column reformed to resume the heartbreaking pursuit of the elusive quarry. The Apache scouts, who had been sent out to the east and west the day before, returned to the command, reporting signs of renegades at widely separated points. A rancher and his family had been murdered at Sulphur Springs, two cowboys had had a running fight with Apaches in San Simon Valley, two men had been killed near Billings' ranch.

A lieutenant with six men and three scouts was sent ahead of the column. Within a mile they were fired upon and driven back. The infantry deployed and advanced after a brief reconnaissance by the grizzled captain. Geronimo had chosen a position impossible for cavalry, impregnable to infantry. His fortifications topped a low but steep hill, the summit of which was already boulder-strewn by nature. On three sides the hill overlooked open country that afforded no shelter within the effective range of the weapons of that day, on the fourth side, behind him, rose rugged mountains that offered him a ready avenue of retreat. Within twenty miles to the north there was no water for the soldiers or their mounts. Ten miles to the south, upon the opposite side of the range, there was plenty of water, but Geronimo sat astride the only trail short of a fifty-mile-long detour around the end of the range.

The infantry advanced. Already that day they had marched twenty miles beneath a blistering sun from the last water. Their lips were parched and blistered, their eyes, their nostrils, their throats were choked with the stinging, impalpable dust of the alkali desert. All day they had groused and cursed and bewailed the fate that had sent them into "this man's army"; but that had been while they were plodding along in the shroud of dust that hung continually about them and with no sign of an enemy about.

Now it was different. All was changed. With the first shot fatigue slipped from them as easily as an old coat, they forgot the hardships and the thirst, they fretted to go as young thoroughbreds at the barrier. And they were young thoroughbreds—these picked men, hard as nails, the flower of the western army. No finer body of men ever underwent crueler hardships in a more savage country, against a more savage and resourceful foe in any country in the world, and none ever got fewer thanks.

On they went, up toward that silent, rock-bound hilltop. There was no cover; they were advancing to the charge. Geronimo waited. He knew that they would underestimate his strength, judging it by what they had developed at the last stand a mile to the north; and he was right. He waited until the blue line was well within range, then he opened on them with all his rifles. A few men fell. The command to charge was given and up the slope the soldiers raced, yelling. In twos and threes they fell beneath the withering fire of the hostiles. It was a useless sacrifice and the retreat was sounded.

Covered by the fire of the cavalry they withdrew and dug themselves in three-fourths of the way down the slope—those that remained of them. Until dark they lay there, sniping, being sniped at, the painted savages yelling taunts and insults at them. Their water was gone, their dead and wounded lay beneath the pitiless sun on the fire-swept slope.

A sergeant, beneath a hail of lead, brought in a wounded officer. Twenty-five years later he was awarded a Congressional Medal, which arrived in time to be pinned on his breast by an attendant at the poor house before he was buried in Potter's Field.

Under the protection of darkness they recovered their dead and those of the wounded who had miraculously survived the determined sniping of the Apaches. The officers held a council. What water there was left was distributed among the infantrymen. The cavalry and the pack train, bearing the wounded, started back across those weary, dusty miles for water. The dead they buried on the field. At dawn the hostiles recommenced their sniping, though the infantry had withdrawn to such a distance that only an occasional bullet fell among them. They did not know that now the entire force opposing them consisted of but three warriors; that the others were miles away to the south. All day they lay there without shelter while the Apaches fired at them at long range and at long intervals.

It was after dark before the cavalry returned. The hostile fire had ceased, but how could the soldiers know that the last of the enemy was miles away upon the southern trail. Geronimo had accomplished all that he had set out to accomplish. He had held up the troops two full days and in that time the Be-don-ko-he, with the exception of a few warriors, had crossed the boundary into Mexico

93

and disappeared in the rugged mazes of the Mother Mountains; and he had done it without losing a man.

XI

WAR CHIEF OF THE BE-DON-KO-HE

SHOZ-DIJIJI liked the new camp which lay in rugged, timbered mountains south of the town of Casas Grandes, in the state of Chihuahua. There was water there and game and the hated soldiers of the pindah lickoyee could not follow. When they had settled down to the routine of camp life he would tie Nejeunee before the tepee of Ish-kay-nay. Just now, with several other braves, he was hunting, for the long march from the north had depleted the stores of the Be-don-ko-he.

For three days the chase continued, covering mountains and plain, and during that time the hunters brought in a variety and abundance of red meats. In many a pot boiled savory stews of venison, antelope, beef or mule, the sweet aroma of cooking food mingling with the scent of the pine forest in the pure air of the high sierras, while below in the plain many a frightened peon huddled his family about him behind the barred door of his adobe shack the while he mourned the loss of his live stock.

Their bellies filled, peace hovering about them, elated by their victory over the soldiers of the white-eyes, the Be-don-ko-he rested in camp. The warriors smoked and gambled, the women worked and gossiped, the children played. Upon distant look-outs sentinels scanned the country for the first sign of an approaching enemy.

The Be-don-ko-he felt secure. But a chain is as strong only as its weakest link. Perhaps a sentinel was shirking; perhaps there were other Indians who knew the Mother Mountains better than the Be-don-ko-he knew them. How else might be explained the long file of armed men creeping upward through a narrow, timbered defile toward the camp of the Apaches? Twenty-four of them were Mexican regulars and with them were forty Indian allies, hereditary enemies of the Be-don-ko-he.

Geronimo sat before a rude brush shelter, smoking, while Sons-ee-ah-ray ground maize in a metate. Ish-kay-nay, sewing beads to the yoke of a buckskin shirt, worked industriously at her side, while Shoz-Dijiji, squatting in the circle, watched the girl's nimble fingers and beautiful face. Several children played about, sometimes listening to the talk of their elders. At a little distance, her back toward them, sat Geronimo's mother-in-law. She took no part in the

95

conversation, never addressed any of them and was never addressed by them, and when necessary to refer to her signs were invariably employed. Notwithstanding the fact that Geronimo was very fond of her he might never speak to her—thus are primitive peoples slaves to custom, even as we.

Shoz-Dijiji was narrating again his encounter with the three white men and the white girl near Billings' ranch.

"Why," asked Geronimo, "did you not kill the white-eyed girl? It was not wise to let her go back to her people and say that she had seen an Apache in war paint."

"Was she very pretty?" demanded Ish-kay-nay.

"Yes," replied Shoz-Dijiji.

"Is that why you did not kill her?" There was a note of jealousy in the girl's voice. She could be jealous of a white woman.

"I did not kill her because I do not make war on women," said Shoz-Dijiji.

"Then you cannot successfully fight the white-eyes," growled old Geronimo, "for they make war on women and children. If you let their women live they will breed more white warriors to fight against your people. They know—that is the reason they kill our women and our children.

"Listen! The soldiers attack our camps, killing our women and our children. They do this today. They have done it always. Listen to the words of Geronimo of the story of Santa Rita, that his father's father had from his father's father. A hundred rains have come and gone and yet the blood is not washed away from the memory of the Shis-Inday or from the hands of the pindah lickoyee.

"A hundred times have the deer mated; a hundred harvests have been gathered since that day. The Mexicans worked the mines of Santa Rita near the headwaters of the Rio Mimbres in those days, and their chief was a pindah lickoyee named Johnson. His heart was bad, but he hid it beneath soft words. He called our chiefs and told them that he was going to give a great feast, asking them to send word to their people.

"Happy, the chiefs dispatched their runners to the scattered camps and villages of the Shis-Inday summoning the people to assemble at the mines on the appointed day. From all directions they came, bringing their women and their children until a thousand Apaches gathered about the barbecue pits of the pindah lickoyee.

"Less than a hundred yards away lay a pile of pack saddles. They looked quite harmless. How were our chiefs to know that hidden beneath them was a cannon, loaded to the muzzle with

96

slugs, musket balls, with nails and pieces of glass? They did not know. The pindah lickoyee lighted the fuse himself. There was a loud noise and several hundred Apache men, women and children lay dead, or maimed and wounded. Then the Mexicans charged us.

"Four hundred were killed. What could our people do? They had come in friendship and peace, leaving their weapons behind. Those who could scattered and escaped.

"Now the pindah lickoyee tell us that it is wicked to kill women and children. They mean that it is wicked to kill the women and children of the lickoyee. It is all right to kill the women and children of the Shis-Inday. But we do not forget. You must not forget. Kill them, that they may not breed warriors to kill your women and children."

"Yes," cried Ish-kay-nay, "kill them!"

"I will kill their warriors," replied Shoz-Dijiji, quietly. "Let the women and the old men kill their women."

Geronimo shook his head. "Wait," he said, "until they have killed your women; then you will have the right to speak."

A volley of rifle fire brought a sudden end to the conversation. Bullets pinged and whistled among the trees. War whoops reverberated among the lofty peaks. The Be-don-ko-he, taken entirely by surprise, scattered like rabbits, the warriors seizing their weapons as they fled. Two fell before they could gain cover.

Geronimo rallied his force and led it forward. Taking advantage of trees and rocks the Apaches advanced against the enemy's line. Shoz-Dijiji fought beside his fierce sire. The war chief led his warriors to within ten yards of the Mexicans and their allies and then, at his command, they stepped into the open from behind rocks and trees and fired point-blank at the foe. At places the lines touched and men fought hand to hand. Geronimo struck down a Mexican with his clubbed rifle, but another sprang upon him with up-raised knife before he could recover himself after delivering the blow. An Indian raised his rifle to the level of Shoz-Dijiji's breast, the muzzle but a few inches away.

It was the proximity of the weapon that saved the son of the war chief from death. With his left forearm he struck up the rifle, grasped it, wrenched it from the grasp of his adversary, and, swinging it behind him, brought it down upon the other's skull; then he wheeled and leaped upon the back of the Mexican who was lunging at Geronimo's breast with his long hunting knife.

A sinewy arm encircled the fellow's neck and he was torn from his prey, whirled about and thrown to the ground. Before he could recover himself a hundred and seventy pounds of steel and iron fell savagely upon him, his knife was wrested from his grasp and he shrieked once as his own blade was buried deep in his heart.

Shoz-Dijiji sprang to his feet, saw the opening that had been made in the enemy's line, saw Gian-nah-tah and another fighting near him, called them and broke through to the rear of the foe. Like a red demon he fell upon the Mexicans and their henchmen; his savage war whoops rose above the din of battle as with the clubbed rifle of an enemy he mowed them down, while the very ferocity of his expression appeared to hold them in a spell of awful fascination.

At last, splattered with the blood and brains of his adversaries, the Black Bear paused. Erect in the midst of the carnage he had wrought he stood like some avenging angel, his fierce eyes casting about for more to slay. There were no more. To the last man the enemy lay dead upon the field, dead or mortally wounded. Already the squaws were moving among them, Shoz-Dijiji thought of the dying women, the mangled children at the copper mines of Santa Rita, and the screams of the tortured brought no answering pity to his heart.

Some warriors gathered about him. He suddenly became aware that they were calling his name aloud; they were acclaiming him. It was unusual, for more often does the Apache boast of his own exploits than those of another; but there could be no mistaking. Geronimo came and laid a hand upon his shoulder. "The warriors of the Be-don-ko-he have chosen Shoz-Dijiji as a war chief," he said, "and they have chosen well."

Then the Black Bear understood. It had come! He thrilled, as what red-blooded man would not thrill to be chosen a war chief by such warriors as these! He had known that it would come—he had dreamed that it was his destiny. This was the first step and it had come years before he had hoped to achieve it. Shoz-Dijiji was very proud, but he was not half as proud as terrible old Geronimo, or as little Ish-kay-nay.

That night moans and wails mingled with the exultations of the victorious tribe, for twelve warriors had fallen in the battle. At the council Shoz-Dijiji's elevation to the rank of war chief was confirmed amidst flights of oratory, and Gian-nah-tah was admitted to the warrior class in recognition of his bravery upon the field of battle.

Their dead buried, the loot gathered from the bodies of the slain foemen, the tribe packed its belongings and set out from this camp, which they called Sko-la-ta, toward the northeast. Through the lofty mountains they made their way, and when they came out down into Sonora they were joined by Juh and a band of Ned-ni.

The two tribes decided to go to the town of Nacosari and trade with the Mexicans.

On an open plain near Nacosari the Apaches were surprised by three companies of Mexican troops, but, after the manner of Apaches when they do not wish to give battle, they scattered in all directions and, firing as they rode away, eluded concerted pursuit. When they had out-distanced the troops they reassembled in the Sierra Madre and held a council. Juh reported having seen Mexican troops at several points and Geronimo well knew that they had been dispatched against him in Chihuahua. It was therefore decided to disband as it would be impossible to maintain a large camp secure from detection while an active campaign was in force against them.

Scattering into single families or small groups of unmarried warriors, they spread out through the mountains of Chihuahua, Sonora, New Mexico and Arizona to await the withdrawal of the troops. For four months they lived by hunting and trading, entering villages as friendly Indians, always careful to commit no depredations, that the fears of the enemy might be lulled into fancied security.

Shoz-Dijiji, happiest when farthest from the haunts of whites, spent all his time hunting in the depth of the mountains. He was much alone, and many were the long nights he spent in some rugged, granite eerie praying to Usen and making strong medicine against future days of war. He dreamed always of war or of Ish-kay-nay or of the goal of his ambition—to be war chief of all the Apaches. The next step, as he planned it, was to become head war chief of the Be-don-ko-he, after Geronimo became too old to lead the tribe in battle, and after that he would win to the final goal.

Occasionally he saw Mexicans in the mountains, and it amused him to wonder what their reaction would be could they guess that a war chief of the Apaches was lying behind a rock or bush above them looking down upon them; but not one of them ever guessed that such potential death lurked thus close.

On several occasions he ventured down upon the plains after antelope. On one of these excursions he had approached a hacienda belonging to a very rich Mexican who owned a herd of horses that was famed throughout all of Mexico, and of which the owner was justly proud. Shoz-Dijiji often watched this herd from a distance as it grazed under the watchful eyes of numerous well-armed vaqueros. It interested him to note the care that was exercised by day and by night to protect the herd against theft; it pleased his vanity to guess that these precautions were directed by fear of his people.

He saw the herd rounded up each afternoon and driven within

99

a walled enclosure, protected by heavy gates; and after dark he came down and prowled about until he was familiar with the surroundings of the hacienda and the habits of its dwellers. He knew when and where they ate and slept, and the hour that the horses were turned out each morning. These things he did not learn in a single visit, but after many visits. He did not know that he might ever put this knowledge to use, but, Apache-like, it suited him to know more of the enemy than the enemy guessed.

In the mountains he had occasionally come upon woodchoppers at work, and when he heard the sounds of their axes he came and watched them, though they never knew that they were watched. He knew where they came to cut wood; he knew the habits of every one of them; he could recognize their faces; he knew how many burros each owned. He knew where they lived and where they took their wood. Whenever it suited him he could kill them—that thought gave him pleasure—but Geronimo had warned them all against depredations of all kinds until the enemy had recovered from the effects of the last raid.

There was one woodchopper who always came alone. He had five burros. All day long he would chop, chop, chop. In the evening he would cook a few beans, smoke a cigarette, roll up in his blanket and sleep until morning. In the morning he would roll a cigarette, cook a few beans, roll another cigarette, load his five burros and start down the trail toward Casas Grandes. Every tenth day Shoz-Dijiji could expect to hear his axe ringing in the forest.

He knew him and his habits so well that he no longer took the trouble to spy upon him. But one day the chopping ceased shortly after it had commenced and there followed a long silence. Shoz-Dijiji was several miles away hunting with bow and arrows. Had the chopping continued all day Shoz-Dijiji would not have given the woodchopper a second thought; but to the suspicious mind of the Apache the silence was ominous. It spoke of a change in the habits of the woodchopper—it augured something new, an altered condition that must be investigated.

Shoz-Dijiji moved quickly but warily among the trees and rocks along the shoulder of a mountain to the point from which he had often watched the woodman in his camp. Looking down he saw the five burros, but at first he saw no woodchopper.

What was that? The Apache cocked an attentive ear. The sound was repeated—a low moan coming up out of the canyon. It was then that Shoz-Dijiji saw a human foot protruding from beneath a felled tree, revealing the lonely tragedy below. He listened intently for several minutes until every sense assured him that there were no other men about, then he descended to the camp, walked around the tree and looked down at the woodchopper.

The Mexican, lying upon his belly, saw the moccasined feet first and guessed the worst, for the moccasins of no two tribes are identical. Turning his head painfully his eyes moved slowly upward to the savage face. With a moan of hopelessness he dropped his head to the ground and commenced to pray. Realizing that not even God could save him from death at the hands of this Apache, he concerned himself only with matters pertaining to the salvation of his immortal soul and to be on the safe side he prayed not only to the gods of his conquerors, but to strange, heathen gods as well— gods whose names were old before Nazareth.

Shoz-Dijiji saw that a not over-large tree had fallen upon the woodchopper, pinioning him in such a way that he could not release himself. He also guessed that the man was injured. Laying hold of the tree the Apache, already a giant in strength, raised it easily from the prostrate form and dragged it to one side. Then he approached the Mexican and with quick, sensitive fingers examined his body and limbs. One leg was broken. Otherwise the man was not seriously hurt. However the broken leg would have proved fatal were help not forthcoming.

The Apache cut away the trouser leg from the injured member, and tore the cloth into strips. He fashioned splints from twigs and small branches, and while his victim screamed he set the broken bones, adjusted the splints, bound them in place with the strips he had torn from the man's trousers.

By this time the Mexican was almost convinced against his better judgment that the Apache did not intend killing him. It was quite inexplicable, but it seemed a fact, and he waxed eloquent in his gratitude; but to all that he said Shoz-Dijiji returned but one reply: "No savvy," albeit he perfectly understood.

He built a soft bed of pine branches and threw up a rude shelter of boughs above the injured man. After that he filled the Mexican's water bottle, placed it beside him and went away as silently as he had come, leaving his hereditary enemy still only half convinced that it was not all part of a diabolical plot to save him for future torture.

Why was it that the Apache did not kill this helpless Mexican? Perhaps he was moved by sentiments of compassion and brotherly love. Far from it. The war chief of all the Apaches had warned them not to kill, that the fears and anger of the foe might be allayed, and that, thus lulled into the lethargy of false peace, they might become easier prey upon the occasion of some future raid.

Shoz-Dijiji hated the Mexican with all the bitterness of his savage nature, but he saw here an opportunity to carry Geronimo's strategy a step further than the wily old chieftain had instructed, and by playing the good Samaritan to impress upon this Mexican and all to whom he should have an opportunity to narrate his adventure that the Apaches not only were not upon the warpath, but were thoroughly friendly.

Just before dark Shoz-Dijiji returned with fresh venison which he cooked and fed to the woodchopper; then he lifted him to the back of one of the burros, unmoved by the screams of agony this necessary handling produced, and, followed by the remaining animals, started down the trail toward the valley, leading the beast upon which the moaning man rode. At times Shoz-Dijiji had to support the Mexican to keep him from falling from his mount, but with infinite patience he pursued the course that he had laid out.

It was dawn when they came to the edge of the village of Casas Grandes. Without a word Shoz-Dijiji dropped the lead rope, turned, and trotted back toward the mountains. When the woodchopper reached his own home and told the story his wife would scarce believe him. Later when the news spread even the chiefs of the village came and questioned him, and a few days later when there were some friendly Indians trading in the town the chiefs spoke to them about this thing and told them that the people of Casas Grandes would like to be friends with the Apaches, but they did not know how to get word to Geronimo.

As it happened these "friendly" Indians were Be-don-ko-he, so the word came promptly to the old chief with the result that a message reached the chiefs of the village of Casas Grandes stating that the Apaches would like to make a treaty of peace with the Mexicans, and runners went out from the camp of Geronimo and the word was carried among the scattered bands. By ones and twos and threes they came from all directions to the appointed place in the mountains above Casas Grandes, and when the day of the treaty making arrived they moved down to the village. Nervous, the chief men met them; nervous, the villagers looked on askance, for the fear of the Apache was as inherent in them as their fear of the devil.

They sat in solemn council, the Mexicans and the Apaches, and there was much talk and hand shaking, during which they all promised to be brothers and fight no more. Afterward they commenced to trade and the Mexicans offered mescal to their guests with a free and generous hand. This innocent looking, but iniquitous beverage is more potent than bullets and it was not long before nearly all the warriors of the Apaches were helpless. It was then that two companies of Mexican troops entered the town and attacked them.

Shoz-Dijiji, asleep behind a corner of an adobe wall, knew nothing of all this until he recovered consciousness the following morning and discovered that he was a prisoner and that twenty of his fellow warriors had been killed in the slaughter of the previous day. He also learned that the women and children of the Be-don-ko-he, who had been taken prisoner, were to be kept as slaves, while he and the other braves were to be shot.

The prisoners were herded together in a corral, surrounded by guards, and the towns-people came and stared at them, or spit upon them, or threw stones at them; the same people with whom they had shaken hands the preceding day. Silent, stoical the Apaches took taunts, insults and hurts without a change of countenance.

Among the other townspeople was a man on crutches, who was accompanied by his wife and several small children. Shoz-Dijiji recognized him immediately as the woodchopper whose life he had saved, but he made no effort to attract the man's attention. What good would it do? Shoz-Dijiji neither sought nor expected favors from the enemy. Gratitude was a quality which he sensed but vaguely, and in his mind it always was confused with self-interest. He could not see how the Mexican might profit by befriending him—therefore there was little likelihood of his doing so.

The woodchopper surveyed the Indians casually. There was nothing remarkable about them except that they were prisoners. It was not often that the Mexicans had Apache prisoners. Presently his eyes alighted upon Shoz-Dijiji. Instant recognition was apparent in them. He nudged his wife and pointed, speaking excitedly.

"There is the Indian who saved my life," he exclaimed, and pressing close to the bars of the corral he sought to attract the attention of the tall brave, standing with folded arms, looking contemptuously at the crowd without.

"Good day, my friend!" called the woodchopper.

Shoz-Dijiji nodded and one of his rare smiles answered the smiling greeting of the Mexican.

"What you doing here?" demanded the latter. "You are a friendly Indian. They have made a mistake. You should tell them. I will tell them."

"No savvy," said Shoz-Dijiji.

An officer, who had heard the statements of the woodchopper, approached him.

"You know this man?" he asked.

"Yes," said the woodchopper, and then he told the officer his story. "Let him go, captain," he begged, "for he is a very good

Indian. He could have killed and robbed me and no one would have known; but instead he fed and brought me home. I do not believe that he is an Apache."

The officer turned to Shoz-Dijiji. "Are you an Apache?" he demanded.

"No savvy," replied the Black Bear.

"You are sure he is the man who saved your life?" demanded the officer.

"I could not know my own mother's face better," the woodchopper assured him.

For several minutes the officer stood in thought before he spoke again.

"I cannot release him," he said, then. "He is to be shot in the morning when the general comes, he and all the other grown men; but it is crowded in this corral and I am afraid with so many prisoners and so few men to guard them that many will escape. Therefore you may take this one and guard him in your own house until morning. If he escapes it will not be my fault."

"Thank you! Thank you!" exclaimed the woodchopper; "and may the Mother of God Bless you."

Shoz-Dijiji heard and understood. He was to live! But not by so much as the quiver of an eyelid did he reveal his understanding. He stood impassive while they bound his hands behind him and placed a rope about his neck, and he followed, though not meekly, but with haughty mien, as the woodchopper led him away, the wife and the several small children following proudly behind.

XII

THE SCALP DANCE

DARKNESS had fallen, but the night was still young when a fire appeared upon the summit of a lonely hill above the village of Casas Grandes. It burned steadily hour after hour, tended by a single, silent figure. Into the hills about and out across the valley it signalled to the scattered braves, and through the silence and the darkness of the night shadowy forms, soft-footed, mysterious, converged toward the shining beacon.

As Shoz-Dijiji kept the signal fire he thought upon the events of the day and he was puzzled. He could not understand why the Mexican had interceded for him, taken him to his home, fed him, and, after dark, turned him loose without any slightest expectation of reward, not even a remote hope of reward. And for the first time in his life, perhaps, there was forced into his consciousness recognition of a quality of the soul of the very existence of which he had hitherto been ignorant—unselfish gratitude.

The Black Bear was a highly intelligent, reasoning human being and so, as he thought the matter out during the long hours of the night, he came to the conclusion that the only motive the woodchopper could have had was prompted by a desire to repay Shoz-Dijiji for his kindness with a like kindness.

Such an attitude of mind directed upon an enemy was at first quite beyond the experience of one Apache-bred and for this reason difficult to grasp fully; but when the facts finally convinced him they induced a certain warmth within his breast that was new and strange. He thought now of the Mexican woodchopper as a brother. He would repay him. If necessary he would lay down his life for him, for to such extremes does the pendulum of the savage heart swing, and none may guess the depth of feeling masked by the trained muscles of the savage Apache face.

Four times from the valley below a coyote yelped and the reveries of Shoz-Dijiji were broken. With four similar yelps he replied. An owl hooted down from the hills behind him; from the north came the scream of a bobcat. And each in turn was answered from the signal fire.

A shadowy form appeared but Shoz-Dijiji was hidden behind a

bush. A whispered word was spoken—a sacred, secret word—and Shoz-Dijiji arose and came forward, greeting a squat, great-chested Be-don-ko-he. One by one, then, they came in about the signal fire—two, three, five, ten—until at last a dozen warriors were gathered.

Shoz-Dijiji picked up some loose stones and arranged them in a line pointing toward the village of Casas Grandes. He leaned them one against another with the sides that had been down, and were marked by contact with the earth, turned upward; that any who might arrive later could read plainly that he who had laid the signal needed assistance in the direction of Casas Grandes. He placed more fuel upon the fire and withdrew to a little distance, followed by the other warriors. There were older warriors and sub-chiefs among them, but they came and listened to Shoz-Dijiji; and when he had finished speaking they signified their willingness to follow him, for not only was he a war chief among them, but he had conceived the plan that he had just explained to them and was therefore entitled to lead whoever agreed to accompany him.

The village of Casas Grandes slept, perhaps a less troubled sleep than it had enjoyed for many a long month, for had not the feared Apaches of the north been routed, had not many of them been killed and many taken prisoner? No wonder the village of Casas Grandes slept in peace as the barefooted soldiers of the guard paced their posts about the prison corral of the Apaches, as a dozen silent forms crept down out of the hills, slinking into the shadows of the little buildings of Casas Grandes, as el general rode swiftly from the south to witness the execution at the coming dawn.

From hidden places about the corral a dozen pairs of savage eyes watched the sleepy sentries pacing to and fro, watched the building that the soldiers were quartered in, waited for the signal from Shoz-Dijiji. At last it came—a figure rushing through the dark, a figure that threw itself upon the nearest sentry with the savage ferocity of a wounded jaguar, wrenching the rifle from astonished hands, striking down the poor peon with brutal savagery. At last Shoz-Dijiji was armed again!

This was the signal! From all sides other men, terrible men, leaped upon the sentinels; but not until the shouts of the Mexicans had alarmed the soldiers in their barracks did the attackers utter a sound, for such had been the orders of Shoz-Dijiji. As the first of the guard turned out they were met by the savage war whoops of the Apaches and a volley of rifle fire that sent them stumbling into momentary retreat. A few braves, detailed by the war chief, leaped into the corral and cut the bonds of the captives. There were a few scattering volleys directed toward the barracks and then silence, as,

106

like the smoke from their own black powder, the Be-don-ko-he merged with the darkness of the night.

Scattering again, the better to throw pursuers off the track, the Apaches were far away from Casas Grandes by morning; and though el general pursued them he lost their trail within two miles of the village, nor ever picked it up again.

It was a long time before the Be-don-ko-he gathered again in the depths of their beloved Arizona mountains and Shoz-Dijiji sat once more in the cool of the evening at the side of Ish-kay-nay. He was a great warrior now and as he recounted his exploits upon the war trail the girl thrilled with pride.

"Tomorrow," he said, "Nejeunee will be tied before the tepee of Ish-kay-nay."

"Not tomorrow," she reminded him, "for tomorrow the izze-nantans purify the warriors who have been upon the war trail and Shoz-Dijiji must ride no other pony then than Nejeunee, his war pony; and Ish-nay-kay will feed no other pony than Nejeunee, the war pony of Shoz-Dijiji."

The young man laughed. "The next day, then," he said.

"The next day," repeated the girl and rubbed her soft cheek against his shoulder caressingly.

The following morning the warriors, wearing their finest raiment, their faces painted with the utmost care, mounted upon their favorite war ponies, assembled below the camp at the edge of the river. Nakay-do-klunni was there with his medicine shirt gorgeous with symbolic paintings, his plumed medicine head-dress, his sash and izze-kloth, ready to make big medicine.

Along the bank of the river, knee to knee, the braves sat their ponies, resplendent with beads and feathers, turquois, silver and painted buckskin. A proud, fierce gathering it was—these savage warriors come to be cleansed of the blood of their foemen.

The izze-nantan waded into the river, cast hoddentin to the four winds, made symbolic passes with his hands, the while he intoned mystic, sacred phrases in a jargon of meaningless gibberish. Then he came forth from the water out upon the bank, impressive, majestic. Going to the warrior at the right of the line he took a weapon from him and returning to the river washed it, dried it, and blew upon it, blowing the ghost of the dead enemy from it.

One after another he repeated this rite for each warrior and then from a buckskin bag at his side he withdrew a few scalps, taken and preserved for this ceremony, which should by ancient custom have been held upon the site of the battle field. Plucking a few hairs from each grisly memento he handed some to each of the warriors all along the line, and while he stood with outstretched hands upraised, mumbling his sacred jargon, each warrior burned the hairs that had been given him, thus purifying forever the tainted air of the battle field which otherwise it would be unsafe to revisit, peopled as it would have been by the malign ghosts of the dead enemy.

Ish-kay-nay stood before the tepee of her father as klego-na-ay rose behind a stunted cedar, a swollen disc of orange flame floating upward out of the mysterious country that lay below the edge of Apacheland.

"Be good, o Moon!" murmured Ish-kay-nay.

"Gun-ju-le, klego-na-ay!" sighed the voices of the Be-don-ko-he women, evening zephyrs sighing through the fragrant cedars.

Little fires crackled merrily, dancing red and orange, shooting sudden tongues of blue, gold-tipped, lighting copper faces old and wrinkled, young and smooth, faces stern and terrible, faces light and laughing; glinting from proud eyes, haughty eyes, cruel eyes, cunning eyes, laughing eyes, beautiful eyes, the eyes of all Apachedom, the eyes of all the world. Laughter, gossip mingled with the crackling of the flames. Little children played pranks upon one another, upon the dogs, upon their elders, unrebuked, and the full moon mounted the clear Apache sky to gaze down, content, upon this living poem of peace and love.

Rising gradually above the confused murmur of the camp the measured voice of the es-a-da-ded arose, insistent. A young brave, gay in the panoply of war, stepped into the firelight dancing to the music of the drum. Naked he was, but for a G-string and moccasins, his god-like body green with copper ore, his face banded with yellow ochre, vermilion, blue; upon his head a war bonnet of eagle feathers; in his hand he bore a lance, a quartz-tipped lance to the point of which was tied something that fluttered as the tip moved— human hair. Shoz-Dijiji bore aloft a trophy in the scalp dance of his people.

Behind him came other braves, painted braves; singing, yelling braves, shouting the savage war whoop that has carried terror down the ages, out of the north, across a world. Grisly tassels waved from many a point. Rifles cracked. Admiring squaws looked on. Ish-kay-nay was among them, her great, dark eyes clinging ever to the mighty figure of her lover.

Weaving in and out among the fires the warriors danced, yelling, until they were upon the verge of exhaustion; but at last it was over—the last scalp had been discarded, a vile thing that no Apache would retain. The camp slept. In far places the scouts watched, guarding against attack. Shoz-Dijiji came among the banked fires, leading Nejeunee. To the tepee of Ish-kay-nay he led him and there he tied him and went away.

In the morning, when Ish-kay-nay arose she looked out and smiled; but she did not come forth until the camp was stirring and there were many about to see her. Others looked at the pinto pony tied there before the tepee, and smiled, too.

At last came Ish-kay-nay, with the carriage of a queen, the step of a panther. She did not hesitate, but taking the rope that held him she led Nejeunee, the war pony of Shoz-Dijiji, to water, and then she fed him. Everyone saw, but there was none that laughed behind his blanket at Ish-kay-nay, or thought her immodest; for there was but one Ish-kay-nay and she could do no wrong, she who all her life had done as she pleased, haughtily indifferent alike to censure or to praise.

There was one wrinkled old warrior who saw, but did not smile. He was the father of Ish-kay-nay. Much would he have preferred Juh, powerful chief of the Ned-ni, as son-in-law; nor as yet was hope dead within him. Later in the day Shoz-Dijiji sought him out, making formal request for the hand of Ish-kay-nay. The old man listened in silence and when Shoz-Dijiji had finished he spoke.

"Ish-kay-nay is a good daughter," he said. "She is strong and can do a good day's work in the fields; there is none who makes better shirts and moccasins; there is none whose bead work is more beautiful; nor any who can prepare food as can Ish-kay-nay. I am growing old. Her loss will be as the loss of my heart. Fifty ponies will not be enough to repay me."

Fifty ponies! Many a daughter of the greatest chiefs there was who had commanded far less. Shoz-Dijiji knew why the price was thus high. The old man believed that it would be so long before Shoz-Dijiji could hope to accumulate that many ponies that he would relinquish his suit and content himself with some other girl whose price was much less; but he did not know the depth of the love that welled in the heart of the son of Geronimo.

"Fifty ponies?" repeated the young warrior.

"Fifty ponies," replied the father of Ish-kay-nay.

Shoz-Dijiji grunted and turned upon his heel. He went at once to Ish-kay-nay.

"Your father demands fifty ponies," he said.

Ish-kay-nay laughed. "Fifty ponies! Why not one hundred—two hundred? Now he will have none, Shoz-Dijiji, for I, Ish-kay-nay, will run away with you."

"No," said the young man. "Shoz-Dijiji has told you before that he does not have to run away with any woman. Shoz-Dijiji is a man;

109

he is a great warrior, a war chief of the Be-don-ko-he; he has led the warriors of his people in battle. Does such a one run away?"

"Shoz-Dijiji does not love Ish-kay-nay," said the girl. "He knows that it will be many, many rains before he can pay fifty ponies to her father. If he loved her he would not want to wait."

"It is because he loves her that he will not make her ashamed before the eyes of our people," replied Shoz-Dijiji. "Do not fear, Ish-kay-nay. Before the next full moon Shoz-Dijiji will have the ponies."

"Where will you get them?"

"Shoz-Dijiji knows. This very day he goes after them. If he does not return before the moon is full again you will know that he is dead. Good-bye, Ish-kay-nay." He drew the girl close to him.

An hour later Ish-kay-nay, standing forlorn upon a rocky promontory, her fringed robe of buckskin fluttering in the breeze, watched a solitary horseman riding toward the south. Her heart was full, but no tear wet her cheek.

Darkness was falling as Nejeunee picked his way across the rocky shoulder of a mountain, a round stone turned beneath his foot, he stumbled and went almost down. When he regained his footing he limped.

Shoz-Dijiji slid from his back and examined the foot and leg, then he remounted and rode on, but more and more did the brave little war pony favor the hurt member. Again Shoz-Dijiji dismounted and felt the tendons of the pastern; there was a swelling there and fever. The Apache arose and slipped the bridle and the blanket from his mount.

"Good-bye, Nejeunee," he said, stroking the pinto's neck. Then he continued on his way alone.

Nejeunee tried to follow, but the leg pained and he stopped. Once he nickered, but Shoz-Dijiji returned no answering whistle. Perplexed, the pinto, limping painfully, hobbled along the rough mountainside after his master. For a mile, perhaps, he followed through the darkness, but at last he stopped, for he could no longer either see or hear Shoz-Dijiji, and the night wind, blowing across the trail, carried the scent spoor away from him. The rising moon looked down upon a little pinto stallion gazing with up-pricked ears toward the south—wistful ears.

On through the night went the Black Bear, down the mountains and across a valley into other mountains. There was no trail where the Black Bear trod; but there were the stars and many familiar landmarks and an uncanny sense that held him to the true course. Hidden deep in these mountains, a parched and barren range, was a large, flat rock, its center hollowed into a basin by some long dead

110

waterfall of antiquity. It lay near the head of a deep and narrow ravine, hidden by a dense thicket.

For a long time it held the rain waters, and for many fiery, dust-choked miles there was no other water. Toward this spot Shoz-Dijiji made his way, as unerringly as the homing pigeon returns to its cote. No other than Apache eyes ever had looked upon this place. A man might die of thirst within twenty feet of it, never guessing that life was just within his grasp.

It was daylight when Shoz-Dijiji came to the water hole. Here, hidden in the dense thicket, he rested, lying up like a savage, hunted beast. Nor is the analogy overdrawn. Further back than goes the memory of man the Apache has been fair prey for his enemies and there has been no closed season. As the wolf, the deer, or the bear he has moved ever in danger of the swift arrow of Navajo or Comanche, of the bullet of the white man. He did not complain. It was a life he understood and loved. It was as fair for him as it was for his enemies, and he prided in the fact that he played it better than they.

Shoz-Dijiji rested but a short time as he wished to push on toward the south, lying up at another place he knew during the heat of the day, timing his marches that he might pass habitations and cross open plains by night, keeping to the mountains in the daylight hours. He carried little food and only a small water bottle, for he could live for months on end upon a country that white men considered waterless and without game. He was armed with a bow and arrows, a knife and a six-shooter.

Upon an excursion of this nature, the success of which depended more upon the agility of his wits than the strength of his armament, he considered a heavy rifle a handicap, and so he had hidden his in a safe cache in the mountains above the Be-don-ko-he camp before he had set out upon his mission.

His water bottle refilled, his own thirst quenched, Shoz-Dijiji clambered up the side of the ravine out of the thicket. Perhaps he was careless; perhaps the wind blew in the wrong direction. However it may have been, the fact remains that the first intimation he had that he was not alone in these arid, deathlike hills was the crack of a rifle and the whistling whing of a rifle ball past his head just as he attained the summit of the rise.

Shoz-Dijiji dropped in his tracks, his body rolling down the steep declivity. Two white men threw themselves flat upon a parallel ridge.

"You got him," said one of them to the other.

"Mebbe there's more of them," replied his companion. "We better wait an' see."

111

They waited for half an hour, watching, listening. From beyond the summit of the ridge they watched there was no sign of life. Behind and slightly above them, upon the main ridge of the mountain, a man lay hid behind a squat shrub, watching them. It was Shoz-Dijiji.

He wished that he had his rifle, for the two lay just out of arrow range and he was a poor shot with a Colt. There was something familiar about one of the men and Shoz-Dijiji wished that he would turn his face that he might have a good look at it, for Shoz-Dijiji never forgot a face, once seen. At last the man did turn. Then it was that the Black Bear recognized him as the survivor of the three who had attacked the white girl near the Billings ranch. Now, more than ever, Shoz-Dijiji wished that he had his rifle. He weighed the wisdom of a revolver shot and put the idea from him. Apachelike he could bide his time against a more favorable opportunity. To fire and miss would be but to disclose his position to the enemy, gaining him nothing, and perhaps causing him still further delay.

He had learned all that he needed to know of these two. They were alone, hunting the yellow iron, doubtless. They had not been following him, but had just chanced upon him. If he did not fire they might lie there a long time waiting and watching, not quite sure that they had killed him, not quite sure that he was not alone. In the meantime Shoz-Dijiji might be far on his way toward the south. Cautiously he slipped down upon the far side of the ridge, well out of their range of vision, rose, turned his face southward and moved silently away, leaving the two prospectors debating the wisdom of a reconnaissance.

A half hour later Shoz-Dijiji came upon their camp. A banked camp fire smoked slightly, some burros, hobbled, stood near by. Shoz-Dijiji paused and brushed the ashes from the fire, then he piled all their belongings quickly upon the coals; he burst the containers in which they had their precious water. This done, he took the hobbles from the burros and drove them ahead of him down the canyon toward the south. Only a short way did he drive them for he well knew that they would need no urging to leave this barren country and search for feed and water.

Continuing his interrupted journey Shoz-Dijiji permitted himself the indulgence of a smile as he considered the plight of the white-eyes. Strangely, perhaps, there was no rancor in his heart against them for having tried to take his life. That was only a part of the game he played, the life-long, savage game of his savage world, the greatest game the world has ever known—man-hunting. He would have done the same as they had an opportunity presented;

112

but he was more patient than they—he could wait until there was no chance of his shot missing.

XIII

"SHOZ-DIJIJI IS DEAD!"

SEVERAL days later Shoz-Dijiji found himself without food or water upon a rough and arid upland dotted with greasewood and sage and an occasional clump of mesquite along the rim of a dry wash. It was fifty miles to a little spring he knew of, and no water had passed his lips for many hours, nor any food; but Shoz-Dijiji was not dismayed. What to us would have meant almost certain death, gave the Apache no concern.

Following the bed of the wash he came near sundown to a place where the mesquite grew thick upon the bank. Here he stopped and dug a hole down through the sand, into moisture, then deeper, making a small basin, into which water filtered very slowly. While the basin filled he occupied himself. Finding a stout mesquite stick he hunted about until he had discovered a pile of twigs and leaves and earth, heaped in seeming disorder among the stems of a large bush. With his stick he beat and belabored the pile. Frightened, hurt, several pack rats emerged, bewildered. These he struck with his club, collecting four; then he returned to the hole he had dug in the sand. Now it contained a cupful of water. With his drinking reed he drew the liquid into his mouth.

Rubbing two sticks together he made a tiny fire beneath the edge of the bank and cooked the pack rats. When he had eaten them there was more water in the basin and again he drank. Carefully he filled the hole that he had made, put out his fire and buried the ashes with the hides and remnants of his repast until there was no sign that an Apache had stopped here to eat and drink. As dusk turned to dark he struck off across the plain toward the purple mountains.

An hour before dawn he was skirting the village of Casas Grandes when he heard voices ahead of him, where no voices should have been at this hour of the night. Stealthily he crept forward to investigate, wormed his way to the top of a little rise of ground and looked down upon a camp of Mexican soldiers. All but the guard were sleeping. A noncommissioned officer was changing sentries and as each was relieved a few words were spoken— these were the voices that he had heard.

Shoz-Dijiji was not looking for Mexican soldiers. They were the last people in the world he cared to meet; and so he gave the camp a wide berth and continued toward the mountains. At dawn he laid up beneath a bush at the top of a low, rocky foothill and slept. Just before noon he was awakened by the thud of horses' feet. Cautiously he peered through the branches of the bush in the direction from which the sound came and saw a patrol of Mexican cavalry riding toward the mountains.

There were three men in the patrol and they were riding directly toward the hill upon the summit of which he lay observing them. He could see from their actions that they did not suspect his presence and that they were following no trail. It was merely a patrol and there were doubtless others out in various directions; it was only chance that had placed him directly upon their post. They would make their circuit and they would return to camp, well pleased if they discovered nothing to delay them, for there were senoritas and a cantina in Casas Grandes and soldiers are soldiers the world over.

Shoz-Dijiji watched them coming. They were handsome men, almost as dark as he, and they sat their horses with an easy grace that bespoke their descent from long lines of vaqueros. The Apache almost had it in him to envy them their gay uniforms and their trappings, but he was too proud to accord them even his envy. He knew that they were brave men and fierce men and that should they discover him, mounted as they were and armed with carbines, there was a chance that he might never drive fifty ponies before the tepee of the father of Ish-kay-nay; that never again might he sit in the cool of the evening beneath the pines that pray, soft-voiced, to Usen, with Ish-kay-nay at his side.

Yes, they were coming directly up the hill! They would ride close beside the bush that hid him now, but would no longer hide him then. Behind him, up toward the great mountains, were other bushes and many rocks. Before they saw him he might run quickly and gain other cover. Perhaps, in this way, he might elude them entirely, letting them pass on upon their business before he resumed his way. Shoz-Dijiji was not looking for Mexican soldiers.

Bent double, running swiftly, keeping the bush he had quit always between himself and the enemy, the Black Bear scurried for new cover, and reached it. They had not seen him—yet. But still they were coming toward him. Again he raced for a new place of concealment, but this time he scarce believed himself that the Mexicans would be so blind as not to discover him, nor were they.

Their sudden shouts shattered the quiet of the noonday; a carbine barked and a bullet ricocheted from a great boulder just as Shoz-Dijiji leaped to shelter behind it.

Shoz-Dijiji whipped out his Colt and fired twice above the top of his rocky breastwork. A horse fell and the three Mexicans scattered for shelter—not because they were cowards, but because they were versed in the guerrilla warfare of their savage foe.

As they scattered, Shoz-Dijiji raced for new shelter, nearer the mountains that were his goal, and again he was fired upon. One of the soldiers was exposed as Shoz-Dijiji turned toward them. Ah, if he had his rifle! But he had no rifle and so he fired with his six-shooter, and though he missed he made all three withdraw behind rocks and bushes, and again he moved quickly to a new location.

For an hour this running fight continued until the Black Bear succeeded in attaining a hilltop so thickly strewn with boulders that he could lie in comparative safety and hold his fortress. If he could but hold it until darkness had come there would be no further need for apprehension; but when he saw one of the soldiers creeping warily back toward the two remaining horses that they had left where the fight commenced he guessed that new trouble lay in store for him, and so he concentrated his fire upon this man.

The other Mexicans, however, had no mind to see their fellow slain and their plan frustrated, so they, in turn, concentrated their fire upon Shoz-Dijiji. Bullets flew thick and fast, pattering upon boulders, plowing into soft earth, ricocheting, whistling, screaming, and the soldier won safely out of range of Shoz-Dijiji's Colt, reached the horses, mounted one of them, and galloped off toward Casas Grandes.

The Apache glanced at the sun, quickly computed the distance to Casas Grandes and the remaining hours of daylight and reached the conclusion that reinforcements would arrive long before dark. His ammunition was running low. Three miles away the mountains offered him sanctuary. It was better to run for them now with only two carbines firing at him than to wait until there were perhaps fifty. He emptied his six-shooter rapidly at the cover behind which the enemy lay; then he reloaded and fired twice again, after which he rose quickly and, bending low, ran for the mountains, zigzagging, dodging, twisting. Bullets whinged past him; bullets spattered him with dirt and gravel; there were bullets everywhere but where Shoz-Dijiji was.

His mind definitely determined upon a plan of action, the Apache did not deviate from it. He passed many places where he might have found shelter and stopped the pursuit, but he ran on, trusting to his speed and the excitement of the soldiers to preserve him from their bullets. He adopted the tactics of the hunted coyote, turning quickly at right angles to his line of retreat where brush grew that would hide him for a moment from his pursuers.

When he emerged again it was to the right or left of where he had disappeared and once again were the soldiers required to relocate their target. Occasionally he turned and fired at them as he ran, which further disconcerted them. When he reached the dense brush at the foot of the first mountain mass he knew that the Mexicans had lost him, and they knew it, too. Reeking with sweat, caked with dust, hot, thirsty, cursing mellifluously, the soldiers squatted, their backs against great rocks, rolling cigarrillos while they waited for reinforcements.

From a high place upon the side of the mountain, Shoz-Dijiji saw them and grinned. He also saw many horsemen galloping toward the hills from Casas Grandes. Again he grinned.

That night he slept in safety deep within the Mother Mountains, far up the side of a mighty peak in a little crevice where a spring rose and sank again before it reached the precipice. Only God, the mountain goat and the Apache had knowledge of this place.

It was cold there and Shoz-Dijiji was almost naked. He was uncomfortable, of course, but the Apache is above discomfort when the call of the war trail sounds. Burning heat by day or freezing cold by night are to him but a part of the game. He does not complain, but prides himself upon his strength to withstand hardship that would destroy the morale of any other warrior in the world, beat him down, weaken him, kill him.

For two weeks Shoz-Dijiji sought his chance to approach the hacienda of the rich Mexican who owned the splendid horses that were known from one end of Mexico to the other; but always there were the soldiers. They seemed to know the purpose of his coming, for patrols appeared to hover constantly about the vicinity of the noble herd, so that the Black Bear had no opportunity for reconnaissance.

Of course they did not know, and it was only chance and the regal hospitality of the rich Mexican that kept them so often and so long where Shoz-Dijiji wished they were not. He fretted and chafed at the delay for the time was almost come when he should be back with the fifty ponies for the father of Ish-kay-nay. Soon the moon would be full again and if he had not come Ish-kay-nay might think him dead.

In Sonora a savage chieftain had been raiding with a handful of his fierce warriors. Now he was slinking northward bearing his loot on stolen mules. It was Juh, chief of the Ned-ni; cruel, relentless Juh; Juh the Butcher. He crossed the Sierra Madre and dropped down into Chihuahua just above Janos. Mexican herders saw him

117

and word was sent to the officer in command of the troops camped by Casas Grandes. Thus did Juh, unguessing, befriend Shoz-Dijiji, for the soldiers broke their camp and rode away toward Janos, leaving the field clear for the Black Bear.

The soldiers did not catch Juh, for that wily old villain pushed on by night and by day until the boundary lay south of him. Then he turned west and entered Arizona and the domain of Na-chi-ta, son of Cochise—the domain of the Cho-kon-en. Here, he had heard, Geronimo was camped with his Be-don-ko-he. There was a very good reason that never left the determined mind of Juh why he wanted to visit the Be-don-ko-he, for he had not relinquished the hope that he might yet win Ish-kay-nay, nor did he care by what means, being as little concerned by questions of ethics as are most white men.

One day his party came upon a little pinto stallion feeding upon the sparse vegetation in the bottom of a coulee, a pinto stallion that looked up and nickered when he caught the familiar scent spoor of his master's people, and then came limping toward them.

Juh recognized Nejeunee and wondered. When the animal followed along with them he made no effort to turn it back, and so he came to the camp of Geronimo with the war pony of Shoz-Dijiji limping in the rear.

The finding of Nejeunee lame and at a distance from the camp of the Be-don-ko-he had set Juh to thinking. It might mean any one of a number of things but particularly it suggested the likelihood of Shoz-Dijiji's absence; for a good war pony is cherished by its owner, and it seemed improbable that if Shoz-Dijiji was with the tribe that he would have permitted his pony to remain thus at the mercy of the first band of raiders, white or red, that might chance upon it. Unquestionably, Shoz-Dijiji had ridden his pony from camp and something, equally unquestionable, had happened to the pony. Perhaps at the same time something had happened to Shoz-Dijiji.

Juh sought the father of Ish-kay-nay and renewed his importuning of the old warrior for the hand of his daughter, nor did he mention Shoz-Dijiji, but he learned all that he wished to know—that Ish-kay-nay had accepted the advances of his rival and that the latter had gone to find the fifty ponies that the old man had demanded.

"He promised Ish-kay-nay that he would return with the full moon," said the old man, "but the time is almost gone and nothing has been heard of him. Perhaps he will not return."

Cunning, unscrupulous, Juh seized upon his opportunity. "He will not return," he said. "Shoz-Dijiji is dead." The old man looked pleased. "In Sonora he was killed by the Mexicans. There we were

118

told that a young warrior had been killed while attempting to drive off a bunch of horses. We did not know who he was until we found his pony. It was lame. We brought it with us. Talk with the girl. If she will feed and water my pony, come to me. Juh will give the father of Ish-kay-nay fifteen ponies."

"The other was to have given me fifty," said the old man.

Juh laughed. "That was talk," he said. "How could he give you fifty ponies when he had but three? I have fifteen ponies; that is better than fifty that do not exist."

"You have more than fifteen ponies," the old man reminded him.

"Yes, I have many more, and I am a great chief. Juh can do many things for the father of Ish-kay-nay."

"Twenty-five ponies," suggested the other, preferring twenty-five ponies to the chance that Juh would forget the less concrete suggestion of future obligation.

"Fifteen ponies and five mules," said Juh.

"Twenty-five ponies. The girl is a good daughter. My heart will be heavy with sorrow when she is gone."

"Twenty ponies and five mules," snapped Juh with finality, turning upon his heel.

"And a rifle," added the father of Ish-kay-nay.

"And a rifle," acquiesced the chief of the Ned-ni.

"And ammunition," exclaimed the old man, hurriedly; but the deal was made on the basis of twenty ponies, five mules and a rifle.

Ish-kay-nay, sitting beneath the shade of a tree, was sewing pretty beads upon a bit of buckskin, using an awl and deer sinew. She hummed contentedly to herself as she planned for the future— the long, happy future with Shoz-Dijiji. She would make many pretty things for them both and for their tepee. Later she would make other pretty things, tiny things, for future war chiefs. Her father found her thus.

"Shoz-Dijiji will not return," he said.

She looked up at him quickly, sensing a new note in a statement that she had already heard many times since her lover had departed. Heretofore the statement had implied only hope, now it was redolent of sweet relief.

"Why?" she asked.

"He is dead."

The heart of Ish-kay-nay went cold and numb within her, but the expression upon her face underwent no change. "Who says so?" she demanded.

"Juh."

119

"Either Juh lies, or he has himself slain Shoz-Dijiji," said the girl.

"Juh does not lie, nor has he slain Shoz-Dijiji." Then he told her all that Juh had told him. "I am an old man," he continued. "I have not long to live. Before I die I would see my daughter, whom I love, safe with a great warrior. Juh is a great warrior. He will treat you well. He has many women and you will not have to work hard. If he ties his pony before our tepee Ish-kay-nay will lead it to water and feed it?"

"I do not believe that Shoz-Dijiji is dead," she said.

"If you did, would you go to Juh?"

"I would not care what became of me if Shoz-Dijiji were dead."

"He is dead," said the old man.

"The moon is not yet full," urged Ish-kay-nay.

"If Shoz-Dijiji has not returned when next klego-na-ay rides across the heavens will Ish-kay-nay listen with favor to the words of Juh?"

"If Shoz-Dijiji has not returned then," she said wearily, "Juh may tie his pony before our tepee. Then Ish-kay-nay will know what to do. She does not give her answer before."

This word the old man bore to Juh and the two had to be satisfied with it, though Juh, knowing Ish-kay-nay of old, would have preferred something more definite as he had no stomach for another public rebuff.

Day after day early morning found an Apache girl standing solitary and sad upon a commanding mountain looking ever with straining eyes out toward the south—looking for a mighty figure, a loved figure, a figure that never came. Sometimes she stood there all day long, watching, waiting.

She hated to go to the tepee of her father, for the old man talked always of Juh and of her duty, of the honor of being the squaw of a great chief; and so she crept there late at night and hid in her blankets, feigning sleep, sleep that would not come. Often she went to another tepee where an aging man and an aging woman sat silent and sorrowing, to the tepee of Geronimo went Ish-kay-nay, mingling her voiceless agony with theirs.

One day old Nakay-do-klunni, the Izze-nan-tan, rode into camp of the Be-don-ko-he and Ish-kay-nay went to him, asking if he could learn from the spirits the truth about her lover; but Nakay-do-klunni was full of another matter and put her off, though not without a thought for business. Perhaps later, he told her, but it would require big medicine and that was expensive. She offered him her little treasures and he promised to see what he could do about it.

When she told her father what she had done he went to Juh and, later, Juh went to Nakay-do-klunni; but Nakay-do-klunni was full of another matter, though he did manage to lay it from his mind temporarily when Juh mentioned a pair of field glasses and a Colt with a mother-of-pearl grip.

"Send the girl to my tepee in the morning," he said to Juh, for that night he was too full of this other matter, and when the evening meal had been eaten and the warriors had gathered to smoke and make talk Nakay-do-klunni told them strange things.

"I had a dream," he said in a voice that all might hear. "The spirits of many izze-nan-tans came and spoke to me and with them were the spirits of all the war chiefs of the Apaches who are yah-ik-tee. And the izze-nantans gave me the power to raise the dead and make them live, and the war chiefs said that they would gather together the spirits of all the warriors who were dead and bring them to the Tonto Basin on a certain day, and that Geronimo, the war chief of all the Apaches, must come there and bring all the living warriors of the six tribes: the warriors of the Be-don-ko-he, of the Chi-hen-ne, of the Sierra Blanca, of the Chi-e-a-hen, of the Cho-kon-en, of the Ned-ni.

"When they are all gathered, the living and the dead, I, Nakay-do-klunni, Izze-nantan of the Shis-Inday, will make the dead warriors to live again so that their numbers will be as the needles upon the pine trees; when they take the war trail the earth will shake and when they raise the war cry the heavens will be rent asunder.

"Upon that night there will be a great feast and a great dance and Nakay-do-klunni will make strong medicine that will turn the bullets of our enemies from the breasts of our warriors; and upon the next day we will take the war path against the white-eyes and they will all be killed and the Shis-Inday will again hold undisputed sway over the country that Usen gave them.

"These are true words and to prove it Nakay-do-klunni will teach the Be-don-ko-he the dance that the spirits of the warriors and their women taught Nakay-do-klunni, the dance that all the peoples of the Shis-Inday will dance upon the great night before they take the war trail against the white-eyes.

"The day is near. Seven times will the sun rise and no more before the day comes when the Shis-Inday will be rid forever of the hated white-eyes and all their kind. Then will the buffalo and the deer and the antelope come back to the country of the Shis-Inday from which the white-eyed men have driven them, and we shall live again as we did in the days of our fathers. I have spoken. Come and I will show you the dance, the spirit dance of your dead."

121

Arranging the warriors and the women in files radiating from a common center, at which he stood, and facing him, so that the formation resembled the spokes of a fellyless wheel of which the izze-nantan was the hub, he started the dancing while two old sub-chiefs beat upon es-a-da-deds. As they danced Nakay-do-klunni chanted weird gibberish and scattered the sacred hoddentin upon the dancers in prodigal profusion and the drummers beat with increasing rapidity.

Occasionally a wild cry would break from the lips of some dancer and be taken up by others until the forest and the mountains rang with the savage sounds. Until morning came and many had dropped with exhaustion the dance continued. The Be-don-ko-he had worked themselves into a frenzy of religious fanaticism, just as had the Cho-kon-en, the Chi-hen-ne and the other tribes that Nakay-do-klunni had visited, just as the old izze-nantan had known that they would.

XIV

"FIFTY APACHES"

IT was nearly noon of the following day before Ish-kay-nay could arouse the exhausted izze-nantan, for the spirit dance had drawn heavily upon his physical resources and, too, it had left him cross and surly; for the cha-ja-la is a hard task master to its devotees, even of a single evening, and Nakay-do-klunni had been steadily at it for weeks in his effort to arouse the scattered tribes. It meant much to Nakay-do-klunni for he had long since sensed the antagonism of the whites toward the members of his precious profession and he saw his powers, and also his emoluments, not alone waning, but approaching total eclipse, if something radical was not compassed to thwart the activities of the pindah lickoyee. Power and emoluments were the life of Nakay-do-klunni.

He glared fiercely at Ish-kay-nay. "What do you want?" he snapped.

"To know if Shoz-Dijiji lives and will return." she said.

Her words reminded the medicine man of something, of a pair of field glasses and a pearl-handled Colt, and he relaxed. "Sit down," he mumbled. "Nakay-do-klunni make medicine, talk with spirits, you wait."

Ish-kay-nay sat down. The medicine man opened a beaded buckskin bag and took forth some pieces of lightning-riven wood, a root, a stone, a piece of turquoise, a glass bead and a square bit of buckskin upon which colored designs had been painted. All the time he mumbled strange words that Ish-kay-nay only knew were sacred, all powerful and terrible. Nakay-do-klunni did not know even this much about them.

He sprinkled hoddentin upon the potent paraphernalia of his wizardry, upon Ish-kay-nay, upon himself; he tossed it to the four winds. Then he pointed toward a bag that Ish-kay-nay clutched in her hand, and grunted. The girl understood, opened the bag and displayed a few bits of the blue-green dukliji, some colored beads— her treasures. Wide-eyed, tearless, she looked at Nakay-do-klunni, wondering, hoping that this would be enough to insure strong medicine from the great izze-nantan—if her all would be enough to bring her word of Shoz-Dijiji, of her lover.

Nakay-do-klunni scraped it all into his palm, examined it,

dropped it into his own bag, then he closed his eyes and sat in silence, as though listening. For several minutes he sat thus and Ish-kay-nay was greatly impressed by this evidence of supernatural power, for was not Nakay-do-klunni even now in communication with the spirits? When he opened his eyes and looked at her little Ish-kay-nay came as near swooning as it is possible to conceive of an Apache. Her lips parted, panting, she awaited the verdict.

"Shoz-Dijiji not come back," announced Nakay-do-klunni. He waited impressively for a moment "Shoz-Dijiji dead!" He started to give her the harrowing details, as explained to him by Juh, but the girl had risen and was walking away. What did Ish-kay-nay care for the details? It was enough to know that Shoz-Dijiji was dead, that he would not come back, that she was never to see him again.

Her face betrayed nothing of the terrifying, withering emotion that scorched her brain. Erect, proud, almost majestic, the little Indian girl walked out of the camp of the Be-don-ko-he and took her sorrow with her. Far up into the mountains she took it, to a place that she and Shoz-Dijiji had known together. Until night she lay there where none might see her, her supple frame racked by sobs, giving herself wholly to her grief; nor all during the long night did she move, but lay there in the awful silence of the mountain, smothering her moans in its rocky bosom.

When she returned to camp in the morning her eyes were swollen, but dry. Her father was waiting for her, anxiously, for suicide, though rare, was not unknown among the Apaches. He told her that upon the second day the tribe was setting out for the Tonto Basin country; that there was going to be war and that all the pindah lickoyee would be killed. Everything would be different then with the Shis-Inday and Juh would be a very great chief indeed, for all the dead Ned-nis would come back and join the tribe. He urged upon her the necessity for immediately accepting the advances of the chief.

Ish-kay-nay was apathetic. She did not care what happened to her now. Without Shoz-Dijiji there could be no happiness. It might then as well be Juh as another. It would please her father. Listlessly she gave her assent. That night the war pony of the chief of the Ned-ni was tethered before her tepee, and when the tribe broke camp to go to Tonto Basin and upon the war trail Juh rode off alone with Ish-kay-nay, up into the hills.

IN the foothills near Casas Grandes Shoz-Dijiji lay watching the herd of the rich Mexican for several days after the troops withdrew, for, being an Apache, he must reconnoiter carefully, painstakingly, before he struck. At night he crept down and watched and listened

124

and planned very close to the corral where the horses were and the house where the vaqueros slept, until he knew the habits and the customs of the men and saw that they had not changed since last he had been there.

Then came the night that he had chosen for the venture. In the silence of the midnight he crept down to the corral, a high-walled enclosure built to protect its valued contents from such as he. Heavy gates, strongly barred and padlocked would have defied the best efforts of several men. This Shoz-Dijiji well knew and so he did not bother with them. When the time came they would open.

He moved directly to the far side of the corral, as far from the sleeping quarters of the vaqueros as possible, and waited there, listening. Satisfied, he leaped and seized the top of the wall, making no noise. In equal silence he drew himself up and very gently lowered his body to the ground inside. The horses nearer him became restless. One of them snorted. Shoz-Dijiji whispered soothingly soft Spanish words. All the time he stood very still and presently the animals quieted.

In half an hour they were accustomed to his presence, were becoming accustomed to his scent. A few approached, sniffing him. Gradually he commenced moving toward the nearest. It walked away, but did not appear to be terrified. For hours Shoz-Dijiji worked patiently. All depended upon his ability to get close to one horse quickly and without terrifying it; but it was almost dawn before he succeeded and quite dawn before he was able to loop a rope about its lower jaw.

It was only a short time thereafter that he heard the vaqueros moving about. Shoz-Dijiji grinned. With all their care there was this one vulnerable point in their daily routine; it consisted in the fact that they were accustomed to turn the herd from the corral before they saddled their own horses that were kept in a smaller enclosure nearby the main corral. The horses went at once to water, close to the hacienda and in plain view, and by the time they had drunk the vaqueros were saddled ready to drive them out onto the range. All this Shoz-Dijiji knew.

Shoz-Dijiji smelled the breakfasts cooking and the aroma of tobacco. Then he heard someone at the gates. It would be one man, always had been; there was no need of more than one to unlock and swing the portals. The gates swung aside. The horses, crowding, jostling one another, went through with heads well raised, effectually blocking from the view of the single vaquero anything that might have been transpiring in the corral behind them, if he had been seeking to discover; but he was seeking to discover

125

nothing. He was only concerned with the business of inhaling his cigarrillo and digesting his breakfast.

Many times had he done this same letting out of the horses of a morning. There was nothing about it and never had been anything about it to focus upon it any interested attention—least not until this morning. Even at first he did not know what an interesting thing was going on there right in the corral almost under his nose, for the horses' heads were held high and he could not have seen beyond them had he looked; furthermore he did not look. So he did not see that a war chief of the Be-don-ko-he, the son of the war chief of all the Apaches, had slipped a naked leg over the back of a bright bay gelding and was lying close along the animal's side.

Most of the horses were out of the corral when the vaquero was startled to hear a war whoop almost in his ears—a war whoop that was immediately followed by the crack of a revolver. The horses were startled, too. Snorting and with heads even higher than before, the last of them rushed through the gateway, terrified. Behind them, whooping, firing a revolver, came a terrifying thing. They broke first into a gallop and then into a mad run, but still the shrieking, howling creature clung to their rear or flank, circling them, turning them, heading them toward the north.

As it passed the startled vaquero he caught a fleeting glimpse of a moccasined foot and a painted face and he drew his six-shooter, but he dared not fire; for did he not know the high value that his master placed upon these dearly beloved animals of his, and could he shoot without endangering some of them? Instead he turned and ran to notify his fellows, but he met them running toward him, attracted by the whoops and the shots. Already the herd was hidden by its own dust cloud.

"Apaches!" shouted the vaquero, but they did not need to be told that—they had heard that dread cry before. "Fifty of them," shouted the man, running toward the small corral where their mounts were confined.

By the time they had saddled and bridled and ridden out the dust cloud was far away, and though they pursued it they were, as experienced Indian fighters should be, keenly on the lookout for an ambuscade. Knowing that there had been fifty warriors in the party that had run off their stock, it was only natural that they should expect a part of that number to lie in wait for them along the way. Of necessity this slowed down the pursuit, but Shoz-Dijiji did not slow down, he kept the herd at top speed as long as he could do so; and even after it tired and was no longer terrified he pushed it hard along the trail that he had chosen.

The horses had been without water since the previous day and

126

they had run for many miles under the ever-increasing heat of the sun. Now it poured down upon them. They were choked with dust and reeked sweat, and the terrible thing behind them would not let them turn back toward water; but presently, toward noon the thing happened that Shoz-Dijiji knew would happen, so carefully does the Apache plan each smallest detail.

Far ahead, miles and miles away, lay water on the trail that Shoz-Dijiji had thus purposely selected, and somehow the horses knew that it was there as horses seem always to know. No longer did the Apache have difficulty in keeping the great herd upon the right trail, in preventing it from turning back. On the contrary his own mount, having carried him half a day, found difficulty in keeping pace with its fellows.

How he took them, alone and unaided, across weary, dusty, burning miles, through scorching deserts and rugged mountains equally scorching, along a trail beset by enemies, pursued by wrathful vaqueros, would well have been the subject of a deathless epic had Shoz-Dijiji lived in the days of Homer.

Rests found him always where there were water and grass, sometimes at the end of a long day, or again at the close of a long night; for Shoz-Dijiji, more tireless than the horses, could travel twenty hours on end, and more if necessary. He caught fleeting moments of sleep while the horses watered and fed, always lying on the trail behind them that they must disturb him if they turned back; and turn back they did on more than a single occasion, causing the Apache many an hour of hard and perilous riding; but he was determined to bring them through without the loss of a single horse if that was humanly possible of accomplishment. He would give the father of Ish-kay-nay fifty horses and he would still have fifty for himself, and fifty such horses as these would make Shoz-Dijiji a rich man.

He thought all of the time about Ish-kay-nay. How proud she would be! For Shoz-Dijiji appreciated well and fully the impressiveness of his exploit. If he had been acclaimed as a great warrior before, this would go far toward establishing him as one of the greatest. Forevermore mothers would tell their children of the bravery and prowess of Shoz-Dijiji, nor was he either mistaken or overvain. Shoz-Dijiji had indeed performed a feat worthy of the greatest heroes of his race.

Already he had crossed the boundary and was safe in the country of the Cho-kon-en, and all that last night he urged the tired horses on that he might reach camp in the morning. His arms and his heart ached for Ish-kay-nay—little Ish-kay-nay, the playfellow of his childhood, the sweetheart of today, the mate of the morrow.

Toward dawn he came to water and let the herd drink. He would rest it there for an hour and then push on, reaching camp before the excessive heat of this early September day had become oppressive. Quenching his own thirst and that of the horse he rode, Shoz-Dijiji lay down to sleep, his crude bridle rein tied to his wrist.

The horses, tired and footsore, were quiet. Some of them browsed a little upon the dried, yellow grasses; many lay down to rest. The sun rose and looked down upon the little mountain meadow, upon the drowsing horses and the sleeping man.

Another looked down, also—a tall, gaunt man with cheeks like parchment and a mustache that had once been red, but was now, from over exposure to the Arizona sun, a sickly straw color. He had a reddish beard that was not yet old enough to have bleached. Upon the blue sleeves of his jacket were yellow chevrons. Sergeant Olson of "D" Troop looked down and saw exactly what the sun saw—an Apache buck, habited for the war trail, asleep beside a bunch of stolen stock. Sergeant Olson needed but a glance to assure his experienced cavalry eye that these were no Indian cayuses.

He withdrew below the edge of the hill from which he had been reconnoitering and transmitted a gesture of silence toward other men dressed in blue who sat their horses below him, and beckoned to an officer who quickly rode upward and dismounted. Presently the officer shared the secret with Sergeant Olson and the sun. He issued whispered orders and forty men rode down a narrow ravine and crossed a ridge into the canyon below Shoz-Dijiji. The sun, crossing the withers of Shoz-Dijiji's horse, shone upon the warrior's face and he awoke. He arose and mounted his horse.

Sergeant Olson, looking down from above, watched him. If he went down the canyon, all right; if he went up, all wrong—there were no soldiers up the canyon. Shoz-Dijiji circled the herd and started it up the canyon. This did not suit Sergeant Olson; anyhow, the only good Indian is a dead Indian. The noncommissioned officer drew his army Colt from its holster, took accurate aim and fired. Who could blame him?

Two days before his bunkie had been shot down in cold blood at Cibicu Creek by an Apache scout who was in the service and the uniform of the United States. He had seen Captain Hentig murdered, shot in the back, by another scout named Mosby; he had seen Bird and Sondergros and Sullivan, and others killed; and, he smiled even then at the recollection, he had seen Ahrens, a "D" Troop bugler, put three bullets into the head of that old devil, Nakay-do- klunni. Sergent Olson called him Bobbydoklinne. Tough old buzzard, he was! Those three forty-fives in his cabezas hadn't killed him, and Smith, another "D" Troup sergeant, had found him

128

crawling about on the ground after dark and had finshed him with an axe—good old Smith!

Shooting down at a considerable angle from a considerable distance above one's target is difficult. No, shooting down is not difficult, but hitting your target is. Sergeant Olson missed. With an oath, he stood up and commenced firing rapidly and Shoz-Dijiji, seeing him immediately, returned the fire. Sergent Olson emitted an explosive oath and dived forward opon the brow of the hill. There he lay, very quiet, while Shoz-Dijiji urged his horse up the steep canyon side opposite. It is the Apache's instinct when surprised to seek some rugged, inaccessible spot from which he can survey witout being surveyed, and always a place difficult or imposible for horses.

From the top of the hogback Shoz-Dijiji looked over at Sergant Olson, who had not moved. He saw no other soldiers there, but he knew where there was one soldier there were others, usually many of them. He cocked his ears. Ah, what was that? From down the canyon came unmistakable evidence of the clumsy approach of clumsy white-eyes. They made enough noise, thought Shoz-Dijiji, to have been a great army, but he knew that they were not. All the members of the six tribes including their women and children could have passed along this same trail with a tenth the commotion—only the soft swish of their moccasined feet.

Shoz-Dijiji hid his horse on the far side of the hogback and crept back to watch. He saw the soldiers come, and hate and disappointment surged through him in hot, savage waves as he watched them round up his hundred horses and drive them back down the canyon, while a detachment from the troop followed upward in search of Indians.

Others went up the opposite side of the canyon to look for Olson; and as they found him Shoz-Dijiji mounted his horse below the edge of the hogback and rode down toward the valley, paralleling the course taken by the soldiers and his horses, loath to give them up, hoping against hope that some circumstance might give him the opportunity to win them back, ready to risk his life, if need be, for the price of Ish-kay-nay and happiness.

Bitter were the thoughts of Shoz-Dijiji as he followed the troopers who had stolen his herd, for by the hoary standards of the Apache, ages old, it was theft and the herd was his. Had he not taken it by virtue of courage and cunning, winning it fairly? Had the soldiers been taking his herd for themselves there would have been less anger in the heart of Shoz-Dijiji, for he could accord to others the same rights that he demanded for himself, but they were not.

Experience had taught him that the fool white-eyes took stock from the Indians and tried to return it to those from whom the

Indians had taken it, profiting in no way. Therefore he believed that they did so purely for the purpose of persecuting the Indians, just as they had taken their water and their lands and ruined their hunting grounds, which was, in the sight of Usen and his children, but a part of the plan of the pindah lickoyee to exterminate the Shis-Inday.

Did not all men know that the thing the pindah lickoyee called government had hired many hunters to exterminate the buffalo and all other game, thus forcing the Indians to remain on the reservations and beg for rations or starve? Bitter were the thoughts of Shoz-Dijiji as he followed the troopers down toward the plain.

From behind a knoll near the mouth of the canyon the Black Bear saw the soldiers of "D" Troop drive the horses out upon the plain and toward the north. As he knew all the vast domain of his people Shoz-Dijiji knew this plain, knew it as he knew the wrinkles in the face of Sons-ee-ah-ray, knew the route the soldiers would take across it, knew the windings of the dry wash that cut deeply through it from the canyon's mouth. He waited where he was until a rise of ground hid him from the troopers entering the plain below. Cautiously the Apache rode down into the wash and along its dry, sandy bottom where the steep, high banks hid him from the sight of the soldiers. Where the wash took a broad sweep to the east he urged his mount to a run. The sand beneath its feet gave forth no dust nor any sound.

The soldiers, moving in a more direct line, were drawing away from him as Shoz-Dijiji raced, a silent shadow, toward the destination he had chosen. The wash turned toward the north and then again in a westerly direction, making a wide curve and coming again very close to the trail along which the soldiers were driving Shoz-Dijiji's herd. Toward this point the Apache was racing, in his mind a bold plan, such a plan as only an Apache mind might conceive—of all warriors the most cautious, also, of all warriors, the most fearless when emergency demanded fearlessness.

Other warriors might pit themselves gallantly and gloriously against great odds in defense of the weak, in furtherance of some lofty ideal or for the honor of a flag; but it remained for an Apache, armed with a six-shooter, a knife, a bow and some arrows, to seriously conceive the idea that he might successfully attack ten fully armed cavalrymen for the sake of some captured loot! But perhaps we are unfair to Shoz-Dijiji, for was there not also Ish-kay-nay?

Where the trail came again close to the wash there was a way up its steep side to the plain above, a way that Shoz-Dijiji knew. It had been made by range stock crossing at this point. When the last of the soldiers had passed it they were startled by aloud Apache

130

whoop and the bark of a six-shooter. Yelling, firing, Shoz-Dijiji charged straight toward the rear of the herd, straight toward the ten mounted troopers. The horses broke into a gallop, frightened by the yells and the shots. The soldiers, sure that there must be other hostiles hiding in the wash, fired at Shoz-Dijiji and then turned their attention toward the point where they expected the main force of the enemy to develop, toward the wash. Shoz-Dijiji, still yelling, drew away behind the racing herd.

But only for a moment were the troopers disconcerted by the suddenness, by the sheer effrontery of the attack. A sergeant raised his carbine to his shoulder, his mount, well-trained, stood motionless as its rider slowly dropped the sights upon the bright bay gelding, already a long shot for a sharpshooter, even at a fixed target.

The sergeant pressed the trigger. There was a puff of smoke from the black powder and the bright bay gelding lurched heavily to the ground, turning a complete somersault, hurling its rider far ahead. Over and over rolled Shoz-Dijiji, still clinging to his precious six-shooter, and came to his feet unhurt. A quick glance showed him the herd well out of his reach. No chance there to gain a new mount. To the rear he saw ten angry cavalrymen spurring toward him, firing as they came.

Shoz-Dijiji was trained to think quickly, and as the bullets hurled up spurts of dust about him he vanished again into the wash that had given him up.

XV

HUNTED

FOLLOWING the battle at Cibicu Creek Juh and his warriors clung to the rear and flanks of the retreating cavalry, menacing, harassing, all through the two nerve-racking days of the march to Fort Apache. As his warriors surrounded the fort, firing constantly upon its defenders, Juh went among the Apaches on the reservation, telling them of the slaying of Nakay-do-klunni, of the great victory he had won at Cibicu Creek, promising them that if they would join him the pindah lickoyee would be destroyed to the last man and the Apaches would again rule supreme over their country; nor, in view of visual proof they had had of the retreat of the soldiers, was it difficult to assure them that their hour had struck.

By morning Fort Apache was surrounded by yelling savages, pouring a rain of fire upon the breastworks that had been hastily thrown up by the troops. Scouting parties were abroad watching for the first sign of the reinforcements that might be expected to come to the rescue of the beleaguered post, and to destroy the civilians who attempted to escape.

Consumed by hatred of the whites, incited by the fiery exhortations of their chiefs and medicine men to the extermination of the foe, these scouting parties scourged the country surrounding Fort Apache with all the zeal of religious fanatics.

At Seven Mile Hill they fell upon three men escaping from the post and after a brisk battle killed them and burned their wagon; a few miles south another party lay in wait for two civilians and shot them from ambush; they killed the mail carrier from Black River station, and shot old Fibs, who had the government beef contract, as he sat in his adobe shack, and ran off all his cattle.

And while the warriors of Juh, chief of the Ned-ni, terrorized the country about Fort Apache his messengers rode to Geronimo and to Na-chi-ta urging the Be-don-ko-he and the Cho-kon-en to join him, and the beating of the es-a-da-ded broke the stillness of the Arizona nights as painted braves leaped and shouted in the frenzy of the war dance the length and breadth of Apacheland.

Up from Fort Thomas rode the first reinforcements for Fort Apache, spurred on by the rumor that Colonel Carr and his entire command had been massacred, while from many a hilltop the Ned-ni scouts watched them and took word to Juh. Gathering their ponies and the stolen herds whose numbers had greatly augmented their own the Ned-ni set out toward the southwest to join with Geronimo and the Be-don-ko-he.

Down toward the border, raiding, massacring, fighting off the pursuing troops, the savage horde moved with a rapidity that is possible only to Apaches in the uptorn, burning country across which they chose to lead the suffering troops. Na-chi-ta joined them with his Cho-kon-en, and there was Mangas and Naniy and Kut-le and many another famous warrior to bring terror and destruction to the pindah lickoyee, and with them went their women, their children and their herds.

Northward, searching for his people, went Shoz-Dijiji, dodging, doubling, hiding like a beast of prey upon which the hunters are closing, for in whatever direction he turned he saw soldiers or signs of soldiers. Never had Shoz-Dijiji seen so many soldiers and they all seemed to be marching in the same direction, toward Fort Apache. The young war chief wondered what this movement of troops portended. Had the reservation Indians arisen, were his people on the warpath, or were the pindah lickoyee planning a surprise attack in force?

Shoz-Dijiji could not know, he could only guess that something momentous was afoot, and that where the soldiers of the pindah lickoyee went there would be Apaches. So he kept to the direction the troops were taking, longing to meet one of his own kind, watching always for signals. Patient is the Apache, but the strain of prolonged apprehension was telling upon the nerves of Shoz-Dijiji. Had it been only a question as to the whereabouts or the fate of the Apache people Shoz-Dijiji would have been less seriously affected; but the whereabouts and the fate of Ish-kay-nay were involved and that was by far a more serious consideration.

It irked Shoz-Dijiji to think of returning empty-handed. He knew the raillery to which he would be subjected and which he must accept in silence. He had failed and so there was nothing to say, for in the pandect of the Apaches there is no justification for failure. It would still have been within the range of possibilities to have picked up some horses were it not for all these soldiers; and so to his other reasons for hating them there was added this other, the further frustration of his marriage plan.

It was, therefore, a rather bitter, bloodthirsty savage who came suddenly face to face with a young white girl where no white girl, young or old, should have been upon this September day in Arizona, with the Apaches burning, killing, ravishing across half a dozen counties. She sat beneath the scant shade of a small bush in a ravine well removed from any trail, and that was why it happened that Shoz-Dijiji was face to face with her before he was aware that there was another human being near.

At sight of him the girl sprang to her feet, drawing her Colt, an act that was duplicated with even greater celerity by the young brave, but neither fired—"Shoz-Dijiji!" exclaimed the girl, lowering the muzzle of her weapon. A sudden, friendly smile illuminated her face. Perhaps it was the smile that saved her from sudden death. Shoz-Dijiji was an Apache. His standards of right and wrong were not as ours, and further, he had only one set, and they applied to his friends—for his relations with the enemies of his people he had none. But there must have been something in that friendly smile that influenced him more surely than all the teachings of his elders, more potent even than all his natural inclinations.

Shoz-Dijiji returned his six-shooter to its holster and smiled back at her.

"Wichita Billings," he said.

"What in the world are you doing here?" demanded the girl. "Don't you know that there are soldiers everywhere hunting the Cheeracows? Oh, I forgot! If you could only sabe."

"Here," thought Shoz-Dijiji, "I may be able to learn what is happening between the soldiers and my people." So, as often happens, the ignorant savage sabed when it was to his interest.

"Me savvy," announced Shoz-Dijiji. "Shoz-Dijiji talk English good."

"Why, you told me when I saw you before that you didn't," exclaimed the girl.

Shoz-Dijiji smiled. "Me savvy," he repeated. "Tell me where all these soldiers go? Where are my people that you call Cheeracows?"

"They've gone out—they're on the warpath—and they're just naturally raisin' hell.

"Didn't you know, or, Shoz-Dijiji, are you with a war party?"

"No, Shoz-Dijiji alone. Been away. Come back. No find people. Shoz-Dijiji is looking for his people, that is all. You tell him. Where are they?"

"They been mostly around Fort Apache," said the girl. "There was a fight at Cibicu Creek and they killed a lot of soldiers. Then they attacked the fort. Old Whoa was leading them."

Shoz-Dijiji, watching the girl as she talked, was struck by her beauty. To him it seemed to have a wonderful quality that he had not noticed upon their previous meeting, even though he had then been impressed by her good looks. If he had not loved Ish-kay-nay

134

with such fierce devotion perhaps he might have seen in Wichita Billings a mate well suited to a great war chief.

"Were many Indians killed at Cibicu Creek?" asked Shoz-Dijiji. "Were their women there with them?"

"I have not heard but just a little of the fight," replied Wichita. "Captain Hentig and some of his men were killed and old Bobby-doklinny."

Shoz-Dijiji knew whom she meant, just as he had known that she referred to Juh when she spoke of Whoa—these white-eyes were most ignorant, they could not pronounce the simplest names.

"Do you know if Geronimo went out?" he asked.

"He wasn't with Whoa at Cibicu but we just heard today that the renegades are on their way toward the border and that Geronimo has joined them. It sure looks like a hard winter. I wish to God we'd never left Kansas. Believe me, the East is good enough for Wichita Billings! Say, Shoz-Dijiji, are you sure you aint a renegade?"

"Shoz-Dijiji friendly," he assured her.

"Then you better come in with me and give yourself up or the soldiers will sure get you. They aint askin' no questions when they see a Cheeracow—they just plug him. You come on in to the ranch with me, there's a detachment of "E" Troop there now, and I'll see that they don't hurt you."

Shoz-Dijiji extended a slow hand and laid it on the girl's arm. His face grew very serious and stern as his dark eyes looked into hers. "Listen, white girl," he said. "Shoz-Dijiji said he is friendly. Shoz-Dijiji does no speak lies. He is friendly—to you. Shoz-Dijiji no harm you. Do not be afraid. But Shoz-Dijiji not friend to the white soldiers. Not friend to the white people—only you.

"Shoz-Dijiji is war chief among the Be-don-ko-he. His place is with the warriors of his people. You say there are soldiers at the hacienda of your father. Go! Tell them that Shoz-Dijiji, war chief among the Be-don-ko-he, is here in the hills. Tell them to try and catch him."

The girl shook her head. "No, Shoz-Dijiji, I will not go and tell them anything. You are my friend. I am your friend. You saved me once. I do not care whether you are a renegade or not. I will not tell them you are here, and if I can help you, I will."

Shoz-Dijiji looked at her in silence for what seemed a long time. He was puzzled. There was some quality possessed by the pindah lickoyee and the Mexicans that it was difficult for him to understand, objectively; yet, all unrealizing, he had just been instinctively practicing it himself. What she said recalled the action of the Mexican woodchopper that time at Casas Grandes; but he sensed no similarity between their friendly gratitude and his

135

forbearance toward this beautiful enemy girl, or knew that his action was partially based on gratitude for a friendly smile and frank trustfulness. He thought he did not harm her simply because he did not wish to. He did not know that he could not have harmed her, that there was a force within him stronger even than his savage training.

"You will help Shoz-Dijiji?" he asked.

"You can bet your boots I will," she assured him. "But how?"

"All night, all day Shoz-Dijiji have no water. There were soldiers at every spring, at every water hole. Shoz-Dijiji wants water and a horse."

"Hungry, too?"

"Apache always hungry," laughed the brave.

"You wait here," she told him.

"Where your horse?" he demanded.

She raised her palms to the level of her shoulders and shrugged. "The old son-of-a-gun pitched me clean off," she said. "That's why I was a-sittin' up here restin'. I been walking close to an hour and I'm dog-tired; but it's only a short jag to the house now. I may have to sneak out with a horse for you, so don't get worried if I ain't back before dark." She started away.

"I go with you," said Shoz-Dijiji.

"Oh, no! The soldiers might see you."

"I go a little way—where I can watch you. Mebbyso bad men around; mebbyso hostiles. Shoz-Dijiji go little way and watch."

Through the hills he went with her, walking ahead as a brave should, until they came within sight of the ranch house. Some cavalry mounts were tied to a corral fence; troopers were lolling in the shade of the bunk house swapping lies with the cowhands. An officer leaned in a back-tilted chair beside the doorway of the ranch house talking with Billings. Only Shoz-Dijiji's eyes and forehead showed above the top of the last hill above the wagon road where it entered the little flat in which stood the main ranch buildings, and they were screened from view by a small bush.

"Go," he said to the girl. "You will be safe now."

"Where will you wait?" she asked. "Here?"

"Yes."

She hesitated, her brow puckered in thought. "If I bring you a horse you will return at once to your tribe?" she demanded.

"Yes."

"If you meet any lone whites on the way will you promise me that you will not kill them?"

"Why?"

136

"I cannot bring you a horse to use in murdering my own people," she said.

He nodded. "Me savvy. Shoz-Dijiji no kill until he find his people. If they on war trail Shoz-Dijiji fight with them. Shoz-Dijiji a war chief. White warriors kill. Apache warriors kill. That is right."

"But you must not kill white people at all."

"All right—you go tell white warriors they must not kill Apaches. They stop, Shoz-Dijiji stop. Now you go get pony for Shoz-Dijiji. Big talk no good now—no can eat—no can ride. Go."

The girl could not but smile as she turned away and rounding the summit of the hill dropped down toward the ranch house in full view of those gathered there. At sight of her they all arose and several started in her direction, her father among them.

"Where in all tarnation you been, Chita?" he demanded when they were close enough for speech. "I thought I told you to stay in town until this fracas blowed over."

"Well, it has blowed over, hasn't it?" she asked. "We heard yesterday that the hostiles was all headed for the border, so I thought I'd come home. I'm sure sick o' them tin-horns in town."

"Where's Buckskin? Why in all tarnation you hoofin' it?"

"Pitched me off a mile or so back yender!" she explained. "I was takin' a short cut through the hills."

"You saw no sign of hostiles, I take it, Miss Billings?" suggested the officer, a young cavalry lieutenant.

"Nary hostile," she replied. The young West Pointer thought what a shame it was that such a pretty girl should pronounce the "i" long; doubtless she said "masakree" too. But how pretty she was! He could not recall having seen such a beauty in a month of Sundays. He hoped the C. o. would keep his detachment at the Billings ranch for a long time.

He had heard Billings and some of the cowhands mention Chita and he had expected to see, if he saw her at all, a raw-boned slattern with large, red hands, and so he was not prepared for the dainty beauty that burst upon his astonished vision. God, what a mother she must have had, thought the lieutenant, appraising Billings; but he felt that he could have enjoyed her more had he been deaf, for he had not yet been of the West a sufficient length of time to accustom his ears to the naive pronunciation of the frontier, so different from his native Bostonese.

The young lieutenant to the contrary, not withstanding, it may not be truthfully said that Wichita Billings was dainty; she was beautiful, yes, but with a certain strength and robustness, a definite self-reliance, that does not perfectly harmonize with the truest conception of daintiness. She was entirely feminine and her hands and feet were small, but they were strong looking hands and she stood squarely upon her two feet in her little high-heeled boots. Her well-moulded jaw was a strong jaw and her laughing eyes were brave without boldness.

No, dainty was not the word; but then, perhaps, Lieutenant Samuel Adams King was influenced not by the Back Bay background of yesterday so much as he was by that nearer background composed of rough cavalrymen and pipe-smoking, tobacco-chewing women of the old frontier. By comparison with these the girl was as dainty as a violet in a cabbage patch, especially when she was pensive, as she often was, or when she was smiling, and she was smiling quite as often as she was pensive, in fact, at almost any time when she was not talking. Then the illusion was shattered.

However, strange as it may seem, Lieutenant King found himself drawing the girl into conversation even though every word, or at least every other word, jangled discordantly upon his cultured nerves. It seemed beyond the pale of remotest possibility that any human being could mispronounce so many words, at least so it seemed to Lieutenant King, and at the same time possess such tonal qualities of voice that it became a pleasure to listen to her murder the English language; and so, when they had reached the ranch house he managed to monopolize her.

Her father had wanted to send a couple of men out after her horse, but she had objected, saying that "the ol' fool" would come in at feeding time, and if he didn't it would be good riddance anyway; but while they were discussing the matter the horse suddenly appeared galloping down the very hill from which Wichita had come a few moments before.

"What in tarnation's the matter with thet cayuse anyways?" demanded Billings. "Acts most like he'd seed a silver tip, or a ghost."

The horse was running rapidly toward the ranch, occasionally casting a backward look toward the hilltop. Wichita Billings knew perfectly what Buckskin had seen.

"Reckon as how you fellers better ride up there," said Billings to the two hands, "an' see what all might be there."

"They ain't nothin' there," said Wichita. "Didn't I jest come from there? The ol' son-of-a-gun's been actin' thet away all day— he's jest plumb loco."

So that was the end of that, much to the girl's relief, and Wichita resumed her talk with the officer; an experience which she enjoyed, for she was avid to learn, and she knew that the average man or woman of the frontier could teach her little along the lines toward which her ambition lay. On several occasions she had met cultured men—men who had stopped at her father's Kansas farm, or at the ranch since they came to Arizona—and she had been vividly conscious of a difference between them and the sort of people to whose society she was accustomed.

From them she had derived her first appreciation of the existence of a thing called conversation and a knowledge of its beauty and its value and its rarity. She had been quick to realize her own lack of conversational ability and ambitious enough to dream of improvement; but dreaming was about as far as she could go. What few books and magazines and newspapers filtered to her remote home she devoured eagerly and they taught her many things, though usually overdrawn. She learned new words, the meanings of which she usually guessed shrewdly enough, for she possessed no dictionary, but there was nothing or no one to teach her how to pronounce either the new words or the old, so that she was never actively aware that she mispronounced them and only vaguely disturbed when she listened to the conversation of a person like Lieutenant King. In truth, when she gave the matter any thought, she was more inclined to regret his weird pronunciation of such common words as "Injun" and "hoss" than to question her own. It was the things he spoke of and the pleasant intonation of his cultured voice that delighted her. Lieutenant King was asking her about herself, which didn't interest her at all, and how long she had lived in Arizona. "Goin' on five year," she replied, "an' I reckon you jes' come out with that last bunch o' shave-tails at the post, didn't you?"

He flushed, for he had not realized how apparent were his youth and the newness of his uniform. "Yes," he said, "I graduated in June and I only joined my regiment a few weeks ago."

"From the States o' course?" she asked.

"Yes, and you?"

"I'm from back East, too," she told him.

"Good! From what part?"

"Kansas."

"Oh."

"What part are you from?"

"Massachusetts."

"Oh."

That seemed a very remote country to Wichita Billings. In her mind it raised a picture of a pink area on a map, bounded on three sides by dotted lines and on the fourth by wavy lines. It had never connected itself in her consciousness with a place that people came from; it was a pink area on a map and nothing more. Now it commenced to take on the semblance of reality.

"Tell me about it," she said.

"About what?" he asked.

"Why Massachusetts, of course. I've never been there," and until supper time she kept him to his pleasurable task of talking about home, of his people, of their ways, of the great things that the men of Massachusetts had accomplished in the history of these United States of America.

Never, thought Lieutenant King, had he had so altogether a wonderful audience, so perfect an afternoon; and Chita, drinking in every word, asking many questions, was thrilled and entertained as she had never been before, so much so that she almost forgot the savage Apache waiting there alone upon the sun-scorched hill. But she did not quite forget him. She knew that she could do nothing until after dark, for there was not a reasonable excuse she could offer for leaving the ranch, and had there been she was quite confident that Lieutenant King would have insisted upon going along. The idea made her smile as she tried to picture the surprise of the young officer should she conduct him to the hilltop into the presence of the painted savage waiting there.

XVI

TO SPIRIT LAND

IT was quite dark when Wichita Billings led an unsaddled pony out of the pasture and toward the hill where she had left Shoz-Dijiji. She had difficulty in escaping the notice of the sentry that had been posted near the corral, but she succeeded, though she was still fearful that some keen-eared Indian veteran might yet hear the soft footfalls of the unshod animal. A short distance from the corral she mounted the pony and continued on her way, over her shoulder a canteen of water and in one hand a bag of food. In her heart she knew that she was doing a dangerous and a foolish thing, but gratitude urged her as well as the knowledge that she had given her word. By day it had seemed less difficult to trust that big, handsome brave; but by night it was easy to recall that he was, after all, a cruel, crafty "Cheeracow." She loosened the Colt in its holster, holding the halter rope and bag of food in one hand, determined to be prepared should the worst eventuate; and then, quite suddenly, out of the darkness ahead, a hundred yards from the base of the hill toward which she was riding, loomed the figure of a man.

"Who's that?" she demanded in a hoarse whisper.

"Shoz-Dijiji," came the soft reply.

"What are you doing here? I thought you were going to wait on top of the hill."

"No good you ride far alone at night. Shoz-Dijiji come down to meet you."

So, after all, her fears had been groundless! "You frightened me," she said.

The Apache laughed. She handed him the canteen and the food and the end of the halter rope.

"Who that chief you talk to so long?" he asked suddenly.

"Oh, that was the officer in command of the detachment."

"Yes, I know—what his name?"

"Why do you want to know?"

"He friend Wichita, isn't he?" demanded Shoz-Dijiji.

"Yes, of course."

"Mebbyso sometime he need Apache friend, eh? Wichita friend. Shoz-Dijiji friend. Shoz-Dijiji like you very much. You kind. Shoz-Dijiji no forget, never."

141

"His name is King," said the girl, "Lieutenant King, 'B' Troop, — th Cavalry."

Without another word the Apache leaped to the back of the pony and rode away into the night and the darkness. Wichita Billings crept back to her father's home. That night she dreamed that Lieutenant King and Shoz-Dijiji were fighting to the death and that she stood there watching them, unable to interfere, equally unable to determine which one she wished to see victorious.

Riding northwest in the direction of Cibicu Creek shortly after dawn the following morning Shoz-Dijiji, his eyes always on the alert, saw a slender column of smoke arising from a far mountaintop in the southwest. Stopping, he watched it for several minutes and during that time it remained a steady column of smoke. It carried its message across the desolate waste to Shoz-Dijiji as it did to other scattered warriors of the six tribes, and Shoz-Dijiji reined his pony toward the southwest.

The Apache kept to the hills and to the trailless places as much as possible, for he knew that the whole world was full of enemies searching for him and his kind, searching with field glasses and with rifles; and he knew, too, that those who were not searching for him would shoot him on sight even more quickly.

As he rode his thoughts often returned to the white girl who had befriended him, but more often did they reach ahead across the broken country to embrace the lithe young figure of Ish-kay-nay with the laughing eyes and the black hair. He knew that she would be disappointed but that she would wait. She would not have to wait long, he promised himself, for what he had accomplished once he could accomplish again. Perhaps this time he would take Gian-nah-tah and some of the other young braves with him. Together they could round up many horses in northern Chihuahua or Sonora.

Toward noon, ascending a slight acclivity, Shoz-Dijiji was suddenly confronted by the head and shoulders of a white man as they topped the ridge from the opposite side. Just for an instant the two faced one another. The Apache saw the surprise and fear that swept into the eyes of the pindah lickoyee, saw him turn and vanish.

Dismounting, the Indian led his pony cautiously forward toward the crest of the ridge; ready in his right hand was his six-shooter, alert his ears, his eyes, his every sense. Beyond that summit he knew there was a precipitous hillside, dropping to the bottom of a canyon. A man on foot might scale it, but it was no place to remain and fight, for there was little footing and no cover. These things his knowledge of the spot told him, assuring him that it would be safe to approach the edge of the declivity and reconnoiter, as the white-eyed one must by this time be at the bottom of the canyon.

Cautiously Shoz-Dijiji peered over the edge, several yards from the spot at which the man had disappeared, knowing as he did that if the latter was waiting to fire at him that his attention would be directed upon the spot from which he had discovered the Indian and not even a few yards to the right or to the left; but there was no one waiting to fire at Shoz-Dijiji. At the foot of the canyon wall lay a young white man—quite motionless he lay in a crumpled heap. A few yards away, tied to a stunted bush, was a saddled pony. Shoz-Dijiji remounted and riding a hundred yards up the rim of the canyon zigzagged down its steep side. The man still lay where he had fallen as Shoz-Dijiji approached him and reined in his pony. The Apache dismounted and stooped to examine the white, first removing the other's revolver from its holster. The man was young, twenty perhaps. He was not dead, as the Indian had at first thought likely, for the canyon wall was high and steep and there were rocks at its base, and it appeared evident that the man had fallen the full distance.

Shoz-Dijiji stood looking at his helpless enemy. His eyes appraised his find in terms of loot; there was a good Colt and many rounds of ammunition, and he had seen a rifle resting in its boot along the side of the tethered pony. Many were the other possessions of the white-eyed one that aroused the cupidity of the swart savage. Shoz-Dijiji fingered the hilt of his hunting knife, a keen butcher knife made in Connecticut for no more sanguinary service than slicing roasts in some quiet New England kitchen. How easy it would be to slit the throat of the hated pindah lickoyee and appropriate his belongings.

It was while Shoz-Dijiji was thinking these thoughts that the young man opened his eyes and looked up into the stern, painted face of the red man. Instinctively the youth reached for his Colt, realized that it was gone, recognized it then in the hands of the Indian, and closed his eyes in despair. He felt sick and he knew that he was badly injured by the fall, how badly he could only guess. He had been without water for two days, he was hopelessly lost, and now that the end had come he was not sure but that after all it was something of a relief. That which caused him the greatest apprehension was his knowledge of the possible manner of his death at the hands of one of these human fiends. His very soul shuddered and shrank from the torture that he knew might be in store for him. Shoz-Dijiji looking down at him recalled his promise to the white girl. He turned to continue his journey, knowing that death must surely overtake the white, and then he stopped. The young man, hearing him move away, had opened his eyes again. He saw the Apache rein in his pony, hesitate, and then wheel back

143

toward him. Again he dismounted at his side, stooped down and felt of his legs lifting them, examining them. He put an arm beneath the youth's shoulders and lifted him to his feet. To the great surprise of the white man he found that he could stand, that his body was not broken in any place. The Indian helped him to walk to his pony and lifted him into the saddle. Then he offered him his canteen, for he had seen that the youth's was empty and, too, he had seen in his drawn face, in his swollen lips, the signs of thirst. The boy seized the canteen greedily and placed it to his lips. Shoz-Dijiji permitted him a brief swallow and then took the water from him. Now all fear had left the white man.

"You friendly Indian, eh John?" he asked.

"Me Chihuicahui!" said Shoz-Dijiji fiercely, proudly, tapping his great chest, knowing that the whites knew the fighting, warlike tribes by that name.

"Holy Moses!" breathed the youth. "You a Cheeracow?"

"You lost?" demanded the Black Bear.

"I shore am," replied the other.

"Come!" commanded the Apache. He urged his pony up the canyon and the steep zigzag trail to the summit. When the white had reached his side the Indian asked, "You savvy Billings ranch?"

"Yes," replied the youth.

Shoz-Dijiji pointed eastward and a little north to where a dim, blue butte was barely visible behind its veil of haze.

"Billings ranch there," he said. "Mebbyso one march." He took the other's empty canteen and poured the remaining water from his own into it. He emptied the cartridges from the chambers of, the white's revolver and rifle into his palm and handed the empty weapons back to their owner; then he wheeled his pony and cantered away. Shoz-Dijiji was taking no chances on the honor of a white man—he knew them too well.

For a long time the young man sat looking after his benefactor, his face reflecting the bewilderment that filled his thoughts.

"Well, ding bust my ornery hide!" he remarked, presently, and turned his horse toward the dim, blue butte beyond the horizon.

So, did Shoz-Dijiji the Be-don-ko-he fulfill his promise to the white girl who had befriended him.

Late that afternoon he lay up for a few hours at a place where there was water and shortly after dark, when he had resumed his way, he came upon the first signs of the southward-bound renegades—a broad, well-marked trail, and over it the spoor of cavalry, pressing close behind. In a few miles, by a rocky hill, he found evidences of an engagement and in the moonlight he read the story writ clear upon the ground, in the dust, among the boulders, of the Apache rear guard that had waited here and stopped the advancing soldiers until the main body of the Indians had moved to safety among the rough hills. He guessed that his people had passed through those hills the previous afternoon and that now, under cover of darkness, they were crossing the valley upon the opposite side with the soldiers of the white-eyes in close pursuit.

Farther on again he came upon a place where the Apaches had commenced to break up into small parties and scatter, but there was the older trail of the herd that moved steadily on toward the border. Shoz-Dijiji judged that it was two days ahead of the main body, doubtless being pushed on toward safety by hard-riding youths and that it would win the border long before the troops.

During the night he heard shots far, far ahead; the soldiers had caught up with one of the scattering bands, or perhaps the Apaches had prepared an ambush for them. The firing lasted for a long time, grew dimmer and then ceased—a running fight, mused Shoz-Dijiji, restless that he was not there. Night fighting was rare; the soldiers must be pressing his people closely.

It was a hard night for Shoz-Dijiji, urging on his tired mount, constantly on the alert for the enemy, chafing under the consequent delay; but at last the day dawned as he emerged upon the southern slope of the mountain range and overlooked the broad valley across which his people should have passed during the night. Far away, near the base of the opposite mountains he saw several columns of dust, but whether they were caused by Apaches or soldiers he could not be sure, though it was doubtless the latter, since the Indians had broken up into small bands that would make little dust.

A few minutes later he came upon the scene of last night's battle. It was marked by the bodies of three cavalry horses, empty cartridge shells, some military accouterment, an Apache head-bandanna. As he rode across the spot where the engagement had been fiercest his eye took in every detail of the field and he was sure that there had been no ambush here, but that his people had been overtaken or surprised. It was not such a place as an Apache war chief would choose to make a stand against an enemy. He was moving on again when something arrested his attention. Always suspicious, instantly on the defensive, he wheeled about to face the direction from which there had come to his ears the faintest of sounds. What was it that had broken the silence of this deserted field of death?

Revolver ready, he waited, listening, for a repetition of the sound, his eyes fixed upon a little clump of bushes two hundred yards away. Again, very faintly, it came to his ears, the sound that

145

had at first attracted his attention, a low moan, vibrant with suffering.

Shoz-Dijiji wheeled his pony and rode diagonally up the side of the hill toward a point where he might overlook the whole field and obtain a view of the ground behind those bushes. If danger lurked there he would know it before he came too close. Fools rush in, but not an Apache.

From his point of vantage he saw a figure huddled upon the ground and recognized it instantly as an Indian. Nowhere else was there a sign of life. Still cautiously, he rode slowly down toward the figure and as he approached; he saw that it was a woman, lying with her face buried in the hollow of an arm. Already, even before he had come close enough to dismount, he recognized something familiar in the contours of that slender body.

Leaping from his mount he ran forward and kneeled beside the woman. Very gently he put an arm beneath her and turned her over. Hot blood gushed against his naked arm. His heart stood still as he looked down into the face of Ish-kay-nay. Her eyes were half closed; she scarcely breathed; only her feeble moans betokened that her poor clay still clung tenaciously to the last, fast ravelling strand of life.

"Ish-kay-nay! My little Ish-kay-nay!" Shoz-Dijiji raised his canteen and poured a few drops of water between her lips. The act recalled the girl who had given him the canteen, and, too, that recalled something else—words that Geronimo had once spoken to him. "Wait," the old war chief had said, "until they have killed your women; then you will have the right to speak."

The savage soul of Shoz-Dijiji rose in protest against the cruelty, the wantonness of this act. What if it had been perpetrated during the darkness of night? What if it might have been but a chance shot? Did not Shoz-Dijiji well know that the revealing light of day, or her sex, would not have protected Ish-kay-nay? Had he not seen the soldiers fire into the tepees where the women and children were?

Revived by the water, Ish-kay-nay slowly opened her eyes and looked into his face. Her lips moved in a low whisper: "Shoz-Dijiji, I am coming!" she said.

"Shoz-Dijiji is here with Ish-kay-nay. Do not fear. You are safe."

The great, dark eyes of Ish-kay-nay opened wider with the return of full consciousness as she gazed wonderingly into the face of her lover.

"You are not dead! Oh, Shoz-Dijiji, he told me that you were dead."

"Who said that Shoz-Dijiji was dead?" he demanded.

146

"Juh."

"Juh lied. Why did he tell you that?"

"So that Ish-kay-nay would go with him."

"You went?"

"I thought that Shoz-Dijiji was dead and I did not care then what happened to me. It made my father happy." The effort to speak sent the blood gushing again from the wound in her breast and Shoz-Dijiji tried to check the flow, to stay the hand of death. She tried to speak again. Slowly, haltingly the words came. "Tell Ish-kay-nay—that you—are not angry, Shoz-Dijiji—that you—still love—Ish-kay-nay."

"Ish-kay-nay did right," he said. "Only Juh did wrong. Shoz-Dijiji loves Ish-kay-nay. Shoz-Dijiji will kill Juh!" For a long time the girl lay silently in his arms, her breathing so faint that at times he thought that it had ceased. Terrible was the anguish of Shoz-Dijiji—silent anguish, all the more terrible because there was no outward manifestation of it —as he looked down into the half-closed, dimming eyes of little Ish-kay-nay.

Once she rallied and looked up at him. "My Shoz-Dijiji," she whispered, and then: "Hold me close!" There was fear in those three words. Never before had Shoz-Dijiji heard a note of fear in the voice of Ish-kay-nay. Very gently the savage warrior pressed the slender body closer. There was a long sigh and Ish-kay-nay went limp in his embrace.

Shoz-Dijiji, war chief among the Be-don-ko-he, buried his face in the soft neck and a single, choking sob convulsed his great frame.

XVII

THE TRAIL AND ITS END

DEEP in the mountains in a lone cave Shoz-Dijiji buried Ish-kay-nay, covered the soft contours of the girlish body with hard, cold rocks, piled more rocks before the entrance to the cave until it was choked; buried light and love and happiness in the grave with his sweetheart.

There, beside her grave he spent two days and two nights—days of mourning, nights of prayer. There he killed the pony he had ridden, that Ish-kay-nay might find a mount ready to carry her to the spirit world. This he did, though she was no warrior, nor a great chief, because to Shoz-Dijiji she was more than either. All the hoddentin he possessed he had sprinkled upon her before he covered her dear form, and with her he had buried his most sacred things: his tzi-daltai and his phylactery of buckskin with its precious contents, even the izze-kloth that Nan-ta-do-tash had blessed for him.

Upon the third day, alone, on foot, with no medicine to protect him from evil spirits or from the weapons or machinations of his enemies, he emerged from the hills, cruel, relentless, stark savage, and turned his face toward the south upon the trail of Juh. For two days he had been without food and for one without water, yet he did not suffer. Forgotten were the sufferings of the flesh in the greater anguish of the soul. Terrible were the days that followed. Scant was food, scant was water; long and hideous were the marches, with only hate and vengeance to buoy his spirits, to goad on his flagging muscles. He lashed his legs with switches of mesquite until they bled; he ate lizards and snakes and prairie mice; he drank stinking water when he drank at all, for there were soldiers everywhere, at every spring and water hole, upon every trail, and he must go on, for beyond the soldiers was Juh, somewhere to the south, somewhere in that vast labyrinth of mountain and desert. No turned stone, no bent twig, no downpressed bit of grass escaped his eye, and each told its story of the passing of the Apaches, of the pursuit of the soldiers. He passed through the line of troops at last, not a difficult thing for an Apache in such rough country as this, and the spoor of the Ned-ni became plainer. He pushed on and discovered soldiers once more ahead of him. Their trail came in from the northeast and

148

he could see that they had been moving rapidly, without pack animals. That night he passed them, a single troop of lean, gaunt fighting men, and he saw them cross the international boundary and enter Mexico.

By dawn he was a good ten miles in advance of them when he became aware of something moving just ahead of him. He saw it dimly from the bottom of a swale as it topped the rise above him. He moved even more cautiously than before, but the figure ahead made no noise either. It was a man on foot and Shoz-Dijiji knew that it must be an Indian; but there were enemies among the Indians as well as among the white men. This might be a Navajo scout and if it were—a terrible expression of cruel anticipation crossed the features of the Black Bear, the nearest he had come to smiling for many a bitter day.

When dawn came suddenly upon them Shoz-Dijiji was looking down from another hilltop upon the figure of an Indian. It was an Apache, but the red head band proclaimed him a scout in the service of the pindah lickoyee; also the quick eyes of Shoz-Dijiji discovered that the man was an old acquaintance from the White Mountain tribe. The Black Bear hailed him. The scout turned with ready carbine, but Shoz-Dijiji was behind a boulder.

"Do not shoot," he said. "It is Shoz-Dijiji, the Be-don-ko-he."

The other lowered the muzzle of his carbine and Shoz-Dijiji stepped from behind the boulder.

"Where is Juh?" demanded Shoz-Dijiji.

The other pointed toward the south.

"There are Ned-ni a few miles ahead," he said, "but Juh is not with them. I talked with them two days ago. I am going to talk with them again. The soldiers will not stop this time at the border. They have orders to follow Juh and Geronimo until they catch them, no matter where they go. This I was going to tell the Ned-ni."

"You are going to join the warriors against the white-eyes?" asked Shoz-Dijiji.

The man shook his head. "No. I return to tell the fool white chief that the Ned-ni have gone in another direction."

"Good!" said Shoz-Dijiji. "But you need not go on. I will tell the Ned-ni where the soldiers are and what orders they have been given. Perhaps they will wait and meet the soldiers. There is a place where the trail runs between the steep walls of a canyon. There the soldiers will be cautious against an attack, but just beyond, where it looks safe again they will be off their guard and there the Ned-ni might wait for them—if you will lead them there. Eh?"

"I will lead them there," he said. Shoz-Dijiji trotted on and the White Mountain Apache turned back to lead the hated white men,

149

that he served, into an ambush. Shocking! Dishonorable! Disgraceful! Yes, of course; but many a civilized man wears a decoration today for betraying the confidence of the enemy. It makes a difference who does it—that is all.

Before noon Shoz-Dijiji overtook the Ned-ni and delivered his message after first discovering that Juh was not with them. They were surprised to see him, for there were many of them who really believed that he was dead. There were only eight warriors and about twice as many women and children. The latter the sub-chief sent ahead while the warriors he disposed in strategic positions at the point where the ambush was to occur, and along their trail came "B" Troop of the —th Cavalry, protected by the Apache scouts ahead and upon the flanks. With his troop rode Lieutenant Samuel Adams King, eager for his first brush with the hostiles, his stay at the Billings ranch having been abruptly terminated the very night that Wichita had led the ewe-necked roan out to Shoz-Dijiji. An hour later a courier had come with orders for Lieutenant King to rejoin the troop with his detachment, and there had followed days of hard riding in an effort to intercept the hostiles before they crossed the boundary into Mexico.

Lieutenant King had preferred the company of Wichita Billings to futile scouting after Indians that one never saw, but this was different. For two days they had been hot on the trail of the renegades, with an engagement constantly imminent, and the young blood of the subaltern coursed hot in anticipation of a brush with the enemy. For four years he had slaved and sweated at the Point in preparation for this, and he prayed now that he would not be cheated out of it at the last minute by the dirty, sneaking Siwashes. Gad! If the cowards would only stand and fight once!

Nasty place for an ambush, thought Lieutenant King, as the troops entered a narrow, steep-walled canyon. Good thing the "old man" had sent flankers along the crest on either side.

Beastly dusty! Rotten idea, to make the second lieutenant ride in rear of the outfit. Some day; he would revise Regulations—lots of things wrong with them. He could see that already and he had only joined up a few weeks before. Now, this was better. They were through that canyon and the dust had a chance to blow somewhere else than down his throat, up his nose and into his eyes.

Crack! Pin-n-ng! Crack! Crack! Pin-n-ng! "Left front into line! Gallop! MARCH! CHARGE!" The high voice of the "old man" rose shrilly above the crack of the hostile rifles, the wild Apache war whoops, the cursing of men, the screams of hit horses.

A ragged, yelling line of blue galloped among the great boulders from behind which the nine warriors poured their deadly fire, and

150

as the hostiles fell back to other cover the captain dismounted his troop and sent one platoon in on foot while the horses were withdrawn to better cover. It was no place for cavalry action—that is why the sub-chief had chosen it.

Lieutenant King found himself crawling along on his belly from rock to rock. Bullets spit at him. He raised himself occasionally and fired, though he seldom saw anything to fire at—a puff of smoke—a bronze shoulder—once a painted face. He was at the left of the line and he thought that by moving farther to the left he could pass the hostiles' right and reach a position where he could enfilade them. Obsessed by this idea, overwhelmed by the sheer joy of battle, he forgot everything else. The men of his own command no longer existed. He was fighting alone. It was his first fight and he was having the time of his young life. He worked his way rapidly ahead and to the left.

From the right of the line his captain caught a fleeting glimpse of him and shouted after him. "MISTER King!" he screamed. "Where in hell are you going? Come back here, you blankety, blank, blank fool!" But in his heart the old man thrilled with pride as MISTER King crawled on toward the hostile line, the commands of his superior lost in the din of the engagement and the excitement of the moment.

Just ahead of him King saw two large rocks, each capable of sheltering a couple of men. They stood about two feet apart and if he could reach them they would offer him almost perfect protection from the enemy's fire while at the same time they commanded his right flank.

What Lieutenant King did not see was the painted savage crouching behind the one farthest to the left, nor did he know that this same warrior had been patiently watching and awaiting his advance.

Reaching the opening between the two King crawled cautiously on, his eyes, his whole attention turning to the right toward the position of the enemy. He had reached a position where he could look around behind the right-hand rock and see several of the warriors lying behind other sheltering boulders to his right; and at that instant a heavy body fell upon him, while simultaneously the captain gave the command to charge.

The troopers leaped to their feet and, yelling like the Apaches themselves, stumbled forward among the thick strewn boulders. King's carbine was torn from his grasp. He struggled to free himself from the clutching fingers and the great weight upon him, and managed to turn over onto his back. Glaring down upon him were two savage eyes set in a hideously painted face. A great butcher

151

knife hovered above his breast. He could hear the shouts of his fellows drawing nearer.

The knife halted, poised in mid-air. He saw the Apache stare intently into his face for an instant and then look up in the direction from which the soldiers were charging. The lieutenant struggled, but the man who held him was a giant in strength. King recalled that some fool had told him that one white man was a match for ten Indians. He wished that he might relinquish his present position to his informant.

Suddenly the brave yanked him to his feet as easily as though King had been a little child, and the officer saw two of the men of his own platoon running toward them. Backing slowly up the hillside the warrior kept King directly in front of him. The other hostiles had fallen back rapidly, leaving two of their number dead. There was only one other Apache retreating up the hillside with King's captor and he was above them now and moving swiftly.

The troopers dared not fire on the brave who was dragging King away with him for fear of hitting the officer, and when the other Apache reached the hilltop and found shelter he opened fire on them, forcing them to cover. A moment later King was dragged over the brow of the hill close to where the other Indian was covering the retreat of his fellow. Here he was relieved of his field glasses and cartridge belt, his carbine and revolver having already been appropriated by his captor.

"Now you kill him?" asked the Ned-ni of Shoz-Dijiji.

"No," replied the Be-don-ko-he.

"Take him along and kill him slow, by and by?" suggested the other.

"No kill," snapped Shoz-Dijiji with finality.

"Why?" demanded the Ned-ni, an ugly look distorting his painted face. "Juh right. Shoz-Dijiji's heart turn to water in face of pindah lickoyee. Good! I kill him." He turned his rifle toward King. There was a flash and a burst of flame and smoke; but they did not come from the rifle of the Ned-ni. He was dead.

King had understood no word of what had passed between the two Apaches, and he had only seen that one of them had prevented the other from killing him, but that he did not understand either. No other eyes than his had seen Shoz-Dijiji kill the Ned-ni, for the hill hid them from the sight of all others upon the field of battle. Now his captor turned toward him.

"You savvy white girl, Billings ranch?" he demanded.

King nodded, puzzled. "She like you," continued the Apache. "Me friend white girl. No kill her friend. You savvy?"

152

"Well, I'll be damned!" ejaculated Lieutenant King. "How did you know me? I never saw you before."

"No, but I see you. Apache see everything, know everything. You see white girl again you tell her Shoz-Dijiji no can return her pony. Him dead."

"Who, Shoz-Dijiji?"

"No, pony. I am Shoz-Dijiji," and he tapped his chest proudly. "Pony dead."

"Oh."

"You tell her by and by. Shoz-Dijiji no can send her pony back; he send back her white-eyed lover instead. You savvy?"

"Why, I'm not her—well, I will be damned!"

"Now I go. You move—Shoz-Dijiji shoot. This time he kill. You savvy?"

"Yes, go ahead; and you needn't think I'll try to get you after what you've done for me," and he glanced at the dead Ned-ni beside them. "But, say, before you go won't you tell me how and where and when you got a pony from Wichita Billings?"

"Me no savvy," stated Shoz-Dijiji, and turning, he leaped swiftly down the hillside to disappear a moment later from the sight of the astonished subaltern.

As Shoz-Dijiji had vanished among the hills so had the other warriors, and as the commanding officer reassembled his troop a crestfallen second lieutenant walked down a hillside and approached his captain. The "old man" was furious at himself because he had ridden directly into an ambush, because he had lost some good men and several horses, but principally because the hostiles had slipped through his fingers with the loss of only two of their number. And so he vented his spleen upon the unfortunate King, who had never guessed until that moment how much contempt, sarcasm and insult could be crowded into that single word "Mister."

He was relieved of duty and ordered into arrest, released and returned to duty, three times in the ensuing fifteen minutes after he rejoined the troop. His spirit was raw and sore, and he conceived for his superior a hatred that he knew would survive this life and several lives to come; but that was because he had been but a few weeks under the "old man." Before that campaign was over Lieutenant King would have ridden jubilantly into the mouth of Hell for him. But just then he did not know that his captain's flow of vitriolic invective and censure but masked the fear the older man had felt when he saw the youth's utter disregard of danger leading him straight into the jaws of death.

The old captain knew a brave man when he saw one and he

153

knew, too, that the steadying influence of experience in active service would make a great Indian fighter of such as his second had proven himself to be, and in the depth of his heart he was very proud of the boy, though he would have rather his tongue had been cut out than to admit it in words. It was his way to win loyalty by deeds, with the result that his men cursed him—and worshipped him.

In the light of what Lieutenant King had heard of the character and customs of Apaches he found it difficult to satisfactorily explain the magnanimity of the very first one it had been his fortune to encounter. He found his preconceived estimate of Apache character hanging in mid-air with all its props kicked from under it, and all he could do was wonder.

Shoz-Dijiji was wondering, too. He knew that he had not acted upon impulse and perhaps that was why his action troubled him in retrospect. He tried to be sorry that he had not slain the hated pindah lickoyee, yet, when he thought of the happiness of the white girl when she learned that her lover had been spared, he was glad that he had not killed him. Too fresh was the wound of his own great grief to permit him to be callous to the possible grief of another in like circumstance, and in this case that other was a friend who had been kind to him. Yes, Shoz-Dijiji was satisfied that he had done right. He would have no regrets. As for the Ned-ni—well, he had earned death by his insult.

Following the fight with "B" Troop the little band of Ned-ni broke up once again into still smaller parties and scattered by ones and twos, so that there remained nothing in the way of a trail for the soldiers to follow. Shoz-Dijiji moved directly south into the Sierra Madre, searching for Juh. To every familiar haunt of the Apache went the silent, terrible figure, searching, ever searching; his sorrowing heart like lead in his bronze breast, his soul a torment of consuming fires of hate.

From many a commanding peak he scanned the country north and south, east and west, through the field glasses he had taken from the young officer, and then one day he came upon the spoor of an Apache in the soft earth beside a bubbling spring. You or I might not have been able to discern that a man had stepped there, but Shoz-Dijiji saw the dim print of an Apache war moccasin. He plucked some of the down-pressed grass and breaking it knew from the condition of the juices within that a man had stood there on the preceding day, and then he sought and quickly found the direction of the other's trail, leading toward the south.

Not again, no matter where it went, did Shoz-Dijiji lose sight of

154

the spoor of him whom he followed. Early the next morning he left it momentarily while he ascended a peak and scanned the mountains to the south. Ah, at last! In the distance, tenuous, vapory blue, almost invisible rose a tiny waft of smoke. Indians! Apaches, doubtless. Ned-ni, perhap Juh! Be good, O Usen! Let it be Juh!

It was noon when Shoz-Dijiji passed silently and unseen the sentries of the Ned-ni and stalked majestically into the camp. His quick eyes took in every detail of the scene. He saw two of Juh's squaws and several of his children, but Juh he did not see. But Juh must be near. His long search was ended.

Warriors gathered about him, asking many questions; surprised to see him in the flesh, whom they had thought dead. He told them of the fight with the white soldiers, of the scattering of the balance of the hostiles; that the troops might be following them down into Mexico. He did not ask for Juh; that was not his way. He waited. Perhaps Juh would come soon, but he was impatient. A terrible thought smote him.

"Were many of the Ned-ni killed when you fought the white-eyes?" he asked.

"No," they told him, "two warriors, whose bodies we brought along and buried, and a squaw was missing." They did not mention her name. Seldom do the Apaches call their dead by name. But there was no need—Shoz-Dijiji knew that they spoke of Ish-kay-nay.

"Was she killed by the soldiers?" asked Shoz-Dijiji.

"We do not know. Juh would not return to find out."

"Juh—he is not here," remarked Shoz-Dijiji, casually. That was as near as he would come to asking where Juh was.

"He is hunting in the mountains," said a warrior, waving an informatory hand in the direction of a rugged ridge above the camp.

Shoz-Dijiji walked away. He could not wait. He went from shelter to shelter, talking, but only to throw off suspicion, for he knew that some of them must guess why he was here. When he could, he slipped away among the trees and moved rapidly up the shoulder of the ridge, diagonally that he might cross the spoor of the man he sought, nor had he long to go before he picked up the imprint of a great moccasin, such a moccasin as Juh might wear.

A human tiger, then, he tracked his prey. Up rugged mountainsides ran the trail, across rocky hogbacks where none but an Apache eye might trace it, down into dank ravines and up again along the bold shoulder of a mighty peak. It was there that Shoz-Dijiji heard something moving just beyond the curve of the mountain ahead of him.

He stopped and listened. The thing was approaching, already he had interpreted it, the sound of moccasined feet moving through low brush. Shoz-Dijiji waited. Two seconds, three, five. The figure of a man loomed suddenly before him. It was Juh. The end of the hate-trail had been reached. Juh was returning to camp.

The chief saw and recognized Shoz-Dijiji instantly. He was armed with bow and arrows and a knife. Shoz-Dijiji carried these and a revolver in addition. The carbine he had cached before he entered the Ned-ni camp.

"What does the Be-don-ko-he here?" demanded Juh.

"I, Shoz-Dijiji, have come to kill a great liar. I have come to kill a great coward who cannot protect his women. I have come to kill Juh."

"You cannot kill Juh," said the older man. "Strong is the medicine of Juh. The bullets of the white-eyes cannot enter the body of Juh—they will bounce back and kill you. Nakay-do-klunni made this medicine himself. Go away, before it kills you."

"Nakay-do-klunni is dead," replied Shoz-Dijiji. "His medicine is no good."

"What he made for Juh is good."

"Shoz-Dijiji will throw away all his weapons except his knife," said the young warrior. "Let Juh do likewise. Then, with his knife Shoz-Dijiji will cut the vile heart of Juh out of his breast."

Juh was a big, strong man. He was afraid of no one in a hand-to-hand encounter, so the other's proposal met with instant approval. With a sneer he tossed aside his bow and arrows and Shoz-Dijiji similarly discarded all his weapons but his knife. Like great fighting cats the two drew closer. Juh taunted and insulted his adversary, after the code Apachean. He applied the vilest epithets to which he could lay his naturally vile tongue to the mother of Shoz-Dijiji, to his father, to his grandmother, to his grandfather, to all his forebears back to the first one, whose dam, according to Juh, had been a mangy coyote; then he vilified the coyote.

Shoz-Dijiji, grim, terrible, silent, crept stealthily toward his lifelong enemy. Juh mistook his silence for an indication of fear. He rushed upon the son of Geronimo thinking to bear him down by the suddenness and weight of his bull-like charge. His plunging knife was struck aside and the two closed, but Shoz-Dijiji gave back no single step. With as great effect Juh might have charged one of the ancient pines that soughed above them.

Each seeking to sink his blade in the flesh of the other, they surged and strained to and fro upon the rocky shoulder of the mountain. Below them yawned an abyss whose sheer granite wall dropped straight a thousand feet to the jagged rocks that formed the debris at its base.

156

"Pindah lickoyee," growled the Ned-ni. "Die, son of a white-eyed man!"

Shoz-Dijiji, the muscles rolling beneath his copper hide, forced his knife hand, inch by inch, downward upon the straining, sweating warrior. Juh tried to break away, but a mighty arm held him—held him as he had been bound with thongs of rawhide.

In his efforts to escape, Juh dragged his antagonist nearer and nearer the edge of that awful precipice waiting silently behind him. Juh did not see, but Shoz-Dijiji saw, and did not care. Rather than permit his enemy to escape the Black Bear would go over with him—to death; perhaps to oblivion, perhaps to Ish-kay-nay. What did it matter? Closer and closer came the sharp point to the breast of Juh. "Speak the truth, Juh, for you are about to die." Shoz-Dijiji spoke for the first time since the duel had begun. "Say that Shoz-Dijiji is no pindah lickoyee."

"Juh speaks the truth," panted the other; "You are white." The Ned-ni, straining with every ounce of strength that he possessed, slowly pushed away the menacing blade. He surged suddenly to the right, almost hurling them both to the ground. It was then that he realized how close they had been to the edge of the abyss. A pebble, struck by his foot, rolled a hand breadth and dropped over the edge. Juh shuddered and tried to draw away, but Shoz-Dijiji, determined never to relinquish his hold until his enemy was dead, even if he must die with him, dragged him relentlessly to the verge again. There they toppled for an instant, Juh trying to pull back and the Black Bear straining to precipitate them both to the rocks below. Now Shoz-Dijiji's feet were upon the very edge of the precipice and his back was toward it. His time had come! Surging backward he threw his feet out over the abyss, bringing all his weight into his effort to drag Juh over with him. The chief of the Ned-ni, seeing death staring him in the face, voiced a single, piercing, horrified shriek and hurled himself backward. For an instant they rocked back and forth upon the brink, and then Juh managed to take a backward step and, for the second, they were saved.

Heaving, straining, dripping sweat that ran down their sleek bodies in rivulets, these men of iron who scarce had ever sweat before—so lean their thews and fatless—struggled, turning, twisting, until once again they stood upon the verge of eternity. This time it was Juh whose back was toward the awful gulf.

Now Shoz-Dijiji was seeking to push him over the edge. So rapt had each been in this pushing and pulling toward and away from the verge that one might have thought each had forgotten the rigid knife-hand clasped in the grip of the other. Perhaps they had, momentarily; but it was Shoz-Dijiji who remembered first. With a twisting, sudden wrench, he tore his wrist free from Juh's grasp.

"Die, Ned-ni!" he growled, glaring into the eyes of his foe. He drove his blade deep into the breast of Juh. "Die! Ish-kay-nay is avenged!"

Again and again the blade sank deep into the heart of the Chief of the Ned-ni, his arms dropped limp, he reeled and tried to speak, to beg for mercy. Then it was that Shoz-Dijiji, the Be-don-ko-he, put both palms against the bloody chest of his antagonist and pushed him backward. Screaming, Juh toppled from the rocky ledge and, turning and twisting, his body fell down, down to the jagged rocks a thousand feet below.

XVIII

THE WAR DANCE

A YOUNG man dismounted in the yard of the Billings ranch and approached the owner who, following the noonday meal, was tip-tilted in an arm chair against the adobe wall of the building, picking his teeth and conversing with his daughter.

"I don't reckon you're the boss?" suggested the young man.

"Yep," said Billings, "I reckon as how I am."

"I don't reckon as how you ain't needin' no hands?"

"What kin you do?"

"I kin ride some, and rope."

"Ben sick?" asked Billings, noting the other's pale face.

"Got lost. Pretty near cashed in. Reckon I would have ef a Siwash hadn't come along an' give me some water. He told me how to reach your ranch—that was nigh onto three weeks ago—then I run into a scoutin' party of reg'lars from the post an' they took me in with I 'em. I ben in the hospital ever since. Worse off'n I thought I was I reckon."

"Three weeks ago?" mused Billings. "You was tarnation lucky that Siwash wasn't no Cheeracow. Thet was jest about when they was goin' out."

"Thet's what gets me," said the youth, "he was a Cheeracow. He told me he was, an' not only that, but he was painted up all right enough for the warpath."

"I reckon you must hev had a touch of fever right then," said Billings, skeptically.

The other laughed. "No," he said, "I was all right in the head; but I'm here to tell you I was pretty near plumb sick when I stuck my ol' head up over the top o' that rise an' seen this here hostile lookin' me right in the eye with his ugly, painted mug. Say, I ken see him right now, a-sittin' there on his ewe-neck roan. I did a back flip down thet hill an' pretty near kilt myself for sure." He grinned broadly at the recollection.

"Three weeks ago—a ewe-neck roan," soliloquized Billings. "Did he have a blaze face?"

Wichita Billings could feel the flush that overspread her face and she was glad that she was standing a little to the rear of her father as she listened eagerly to the conversation.

"Yep," affirmed the young man, "he had a blaze face."

Billings half turned toward his daughter. "Now how in all tarnation did that Siwash git a-holt of that cayuse?" he demanded. "Musta took it out o' the c'ral right under the noses o' those there soldiers. I missed that critter the next mornin' an' I never ben able to see what in all tarnation become of him. Thet beats me!"

"Well, I reckon your hoss is down Sonora way somewheres by now," said the youth.

"Fed?" inquired Billings.

"Nope."

"Dump your roll off at the bunk house and turn your hoss into the fust c'ral there," Billings directed. "I'll have the chink rustle you some grub. You ken go to work in the mornin'.."

"What I can't understand," said Billings, when he had come back from the kitchen, "is why that Siwash didn't plug that kid."

"Maybe they ain't all bad, Dad," said Wichita, who thought that she understood perfectly why Shoz-Dijiji had not killed the boy.

"No," admitted her father, "the dead ones ain't so bad."

His vengeance accomplished, Shoz-Dijiji was as a lost soul wandering in Purgatory, facing a goalless eternity. He ranged northern Sonora, a solitary figure, grim, terrible. He avoided Indians as sedulously as he did Mexicans, for the greatest wrong that had ever been done him had been committed by the hand of an Indian. He felt that all men were his enemies and that henceforth he must travel alone. He could not know that the wound, so fresh, so raw, the first hurt that ever had touched his inmost soul, might be healed by the patient hand of Time; that though the scar remained the wound would cease to throb.

He lived by the chase, supplemented by an occasional raid when he required such luxuries as sugar or tobacco, or necessities such as salt, flour or ammunition. Upon these occasions he walked boldly and in the broad light of day into isolated ranch house or village store, taking what he would; where he met with interference he killed, striking swiftly, mercilessly, otherwise he ignored the natives. They were as the dirt beneath his feet, for was he not an Apache, a war chief?

Pride of caste gripped him inflexibly, so that he felt only contempt for those who were not Apaches. Even though the words of Juh were constantly in his mind he pretended that they were not. He thought of himself more jealously than ever as a pure-blooded Apache; the wicked words of Juh were a lie: "You are white!"

Weeks came and went until they numbered months. "The Apache Devil" was notorious across Sonora and into Chihuahua. Whole regiments of Mexican troops were in the field, searching for him; but they never saw him. Strange tales grew up about him. He possessed the power of invisibility. He could change himself at will into a coyote, a rattlesnake, a lion. Every depredation, every murder was attributed to him, until the crimes upon his soul were legion.

Slowly the wound was healing. He was surprised, almost hurt, to discover a growing longing for the companionship of his kind. His thoughts, now, were more and more often filled with pleasant memories of Sons-ee-ah-ray, memories of Geronimo, of the other Be-don-ko-he who were his own people. He wondered how they fared. And then one morning he turned his face northward toward Arizona.

Old Nakay-do-klunni, the trouble maker, was dead; the renegades had returned to the reservations or been driven in scattered bands across the boundary into Mexico. The troops were enjoying a well-earned rest. They were building roads, digging boulders out of parade grounds, erecting telegraph lines up and down over red-hot mountains and white-hot plains, until an entire troop would not have rendered out a teacupful of fat. Always there were detachments scouting, patrolling.

Lieutenant King commanded a detachment thus engaged. A parched, gaunt, service sergeant was, nominally, second in command. He had forgotten more about soldiering and Indian fighting than all the shave-tail second lieutenants in the army knew, and Lieutenant King, by way of becoming a good officer, realized this and utilized the sergeant for the very purpose for which the "old man" had sent him along—as mentor, guide, instructor. However, the sergeant agreed when Lieutenant King suggested that it might not be a bad plan to patrol a little in the direction of Billings ranch, for the sergeant had delicious memories of the prune pies of the Billing's Chinese cook. Arizona nights can be quite the softest, loveliest nights in all the world, and Lieutenant King thought that this was such a one as he sat in the dark shade of a great cottonwood before the Billings ranch house where he could glimpse the half profile of the girl in the light filtering through a window from an oil lamp burning within the building. Beyond the girl, down beside the corrals, twinkled the camp fire of his men and, subdued, there floated to his ears the sound of voices, laughter, the music of a harmonica.

"There is something I want to ask you, Chita," he said, presently. He had discovered that everyone called her Chita, that it embarrassed her and everyone within earshot when he addressed her as Miss Billings.

"Shoot," said Chita. He wished that she would not be so disconcerting. Sitting and looking at that profile that any goddess

161

might well have envied put one in a mood—a delicious, exalted mood—but "shoot" and other conversational peculiarities tended to shatter illusions. He was silent, therefore, rearranging his thoughts to an altered mood.

"Well," she inquired presently, "what's eatin' you?"

King shook his head and grinned. It was no use. "What is consuming me," he said, "is curiosity."

"That's what killed the cat," she returned, laughing. "It ain't a good thing to encourage out this away."

"So I've heard. If one asks personal questions, one is apt to get shot, eh?"

"Yes, or if two asks 'em." she laughed.

"Well, please don't shoot me until you have told me if you know an Apache called Shoz-Dijiji."

"Yes, why?" He thought her tone suddenly constrained, and he noted how quickly she turned and looked him full in the eyes. Even in the dark he felt the intensity of her gaze. "We had a little brush with them just south of the border," he explained. "This fellow captured me. He could easily have killed me. In fact he was about to when he seemed to recognize me. He let me go because I was a friend of yours. He even killed another buck who tried to shoot me. He said you had been kind to him."

"Yes," said the girl. "He saved me once from a tin-horn who was tryin' to get fresh. After that I had a chance to help him once. I'm mighty glad I did."

"So am I—it saved my life. He sent you a message."

"Yes?"

"He said that he could not return your pony because it was dead, but that he would send your friend back alive instead—he seemed to take it for granted that I am your friend."

"Ain't you?"

"I hope so, Chita."

"'Twasn't such a bad swap at that," laughed the girl. "That ewe-neck roan was a sort o' ornery critter anyways; but Dad did seem to set a heap o' store by it—anyways after it was gone. I never heered him do anything but cuss it before."

"He'll probably always think it worth more than a soldier," said King.

"I wouldn't say that, and I wouldn't give him no chance to think about it at all. I reckon Dad wouldn't be tickled more'n half to death if he knew I'd give a hoss to an Injun."

"You must have had a good reason to do it."

"I sure did—I wanted to; but there was really a better reason than that. This was the whitest Injun I ever see and I owed him something for what he'd done for me. I couldn't let a Injun be whiter than me, could I? Listen—I'll tell you all about it."

When she had finished she waited, looking up at King for an expression of his verdict upon her action.

"I think you did right, Chita," he said, "but I also think that the less said about it the better. Don't you?"

"I aint been publishin' the matter in no newspapers," she returned. "You pumped it out of me."

They sat in silence for a long time then, and as King watched her face, the easy, graceful motions of her lithe body, her slender fingers, her dainty ankles, he was drawn to her as he had never been drawn to a woman before. He knew her heart and soul must be as wonderful as her face and form; he had caught a fleeting glimpse of them as she spoke of Shoz-Dijiji and the loyalty that she owed him. What a wonderful creature she would have made had she been born to such an environment of culture and refinement as had surrounded him from childhood. He wanted to reach out and touch her, to draw her toward him, to ask her if he might hope. He was hopelessly, helplessly under the spell of her charms.

"I reckon, mister, I'll be hittin' the hay," she said, rising.

"Chita!" he cried. "Why do you do it?"

"Do what—go to bed?"

"No, not that. Listen to me, Chita. I may offend you—I certainly don't want to, but I can't sit here and look at you and then listen to you and not speak."

"You got me chokin' leather," she admitted, "and I'm two jumps behind at that."

"I suppose you know that you are a very beautiful girl," he said. "Beside your beauty you have character, intelligence, a wonderful heart. But—" he hesitated. It was going to be hard to say and he was already regretting that he had started it.

"Well," she said, "but what? I ain't committed no murders."

"I haven't any right to say what I started to say to you, Chita; except that I—well, Chita, I think you're the most wonderful girl I ever met and I want you to be right in every way."

"I reckon I know what you mean," she said. "We don't talk alike. I know it. You ain't a-goin' to hurt my feelings, because I know you ain't makin' fun of me—and I wouldn't even care if you did, if you'd help me. I was born on a farm in Kansas and what school they was was too fer off to go to only a few weeks in the fall and spring. I didn't learn much of nothin' there. Maw died when I was little. Dad learned me all he knew—how to read and write a little and figger. If I only had somethin' decent to read, or educated folks to talk to me.

I know I got it in me to be—to be different. If there was only some way."

"There is a way," said King, who had been thinking very hard for the past several minutes. "There is a way."

"What?"

"There are some very wonderful women at the post—refined, cultured, educated women, the wife of my troop commander, for instance. One of them would be glad to have you come there. Anyone of them would help you. Would you come, Chita?"

"As what?"

"As the guest of one of these ladies?"

"I don't know none of 'em. I don't think they'd want me."

"Yes they would. The Captain's wife is an old friend of my mother's. She's been wonderful to me since I joined and I know she'd love to have you. These women get terribly lonesome way out here, especially when their husbands are in the field. You would be a Godsend to Mrs. Cullis."

And that is how it happened that Wichita Billings came to Fort Thomas as the guest and ward of Margaret Cullis. Her beauty, her eagerness to learn disarmed all criticism, forestalled all ridicule—the one thing that Wichita Billings could not have survived, the thing that she had feared most. Yet she made so much fun of her own crude diction that those who might have otherwise found in her a target for witty thrusts were the first to defend her.

❦❦❦

Up out of Sonora came Shoz-Dijiji, searching for his people. With him he brought a dozen ponies and some mules, toll that he had collected from the enemy in northern Sonora and southern Arizona. Behind him he left a few smoking piles of embers where homes had been or wagons, a few new corpses, killed without torture, left without mutilation.

The Be-don-ko-he welcomed him without enthusiasm. He took his place among them as though he had not been away. The mules he gave for a great feast and he had presents for Geronimo, Gian-nah-tah and Sons-ee-ah-ray. Ish-kay-nay they did not mention, nor did he. Sorrow, parting, death are but a part of the pathetic tragedy that marks the passing of the Indian; they had taken no greater toll of Shoz-Dijiji than of many another of his tribe. Why then should he flaunt his sorrow in the faces of those whose burdens were as great as his?

Of his warlike deeds, he spoke sparingly, though he was too much the Apache brave to ignore them entirely; but there had come

164

word of his doings out of Mexico and his rating became second to none among all the six tribes. Geronimo was very proud of him.

Restless, Shoz-Dijiji wandered much, and often Gian-nah-tah accompanied him. They hunted together, they visited other tribes. Where there was a great dance or a feast there was Shoz-Dijiji. One night he came to the camp of the Cho-kon-en as the warriors were gathering around the council fire, and Na-chi-ta welcomed him and made a place for him at his side.

"The son of Geronimo has come at a good time," said the chief of the Cho-kon-en. "The young men are restless. They want to go out upon the war trail against the pindah lickoyee. Some of them have been punished by the soldiers for things which were done by no Apache. Always the Apaches are blamed for whatever wrong is done in our land. If there were no white-eyes here we could live in peace. The young men want to fight."

A warrior arose and spoke when the chief had signified that he had finished. For a long time he narrated the wrongs to which the Indians had been subjected, telling the same old story that they all knew so well but which never failed to find an eager and sympathetic audience. He urged the warriors to prepare for battle.

A very old man spoke next. He spoke of the great numbers of the white-eyes, of their power and wealth. He advised against taking the war trail against them.

Thus were several hours consumed and when a vote was taken the majority spoke for war.

"Take this word to Geronimo and the warriors of the Be-don-ko-he," said Na-chi-ta to Shoz-Dijiji, "and ask them if they will join the Cho-kon-en upon the war trail. We will send runners to the other tribes and when the war drum sounds we will gather here again for a great dance that the izze-nantans may make strong medicine and the warriors of the six tribes go forth to battle protected against the weapons of the enemy."

When Shoz-Dijiji returned again to the camp of the Be-don-ko-he he laid Na-chi-ta's proposition before Geronimo, but the old chief shook his head.

"My son," he said, "I am an old man. Many times have I been upon the war trail. Many times have I fought the pindah lickoyee, and always, as the years go by, the pindah lickoyee increase in numbers and grow stronger and the Shis-Inday became fewer in numbers and grow weaker. It has been long time since we defeated the pindah lickoyee in battle; and when we did it made no difference, they came again with more soldiers. If we could not drive them out of our country when we were many and they were few,

165

how could we hope to drive them out now that they are many and we are few?

"Geronimo is war chief of all the Apaches. Geronimo loves his people. He loves his land. He hates the pindah lickoyee. But Geronimo is old and he has the wisdom of the old, he knows when there is no longer hope. My son, for the Apaches there is no hope. Geronimo will never again fight against the pindah lickoyee. Geronimo has spoken."

"Geronimo is right," replied Shoz-Dijiji. "There is no hope. They have taken our land from us; they have taken the game we hunted that we might live; but one thing they cannot take from us—the right to die and to choose the manner of our dying. I, Shoz-Dijiji, choose to die fighting the pindah lickoyee. I shall go out upon the war trail with Na-chi-ta and the Cho-kon-en. I have spoken."

"You have spoken well, my son. You are a young man. Young men should fight. Geronimo is old and tired and very sad. He would rather lay down his weapons and rest."

Great was the activity in the camp of the Cho-kon-en when Shoz-Dijiji returned accompanied by Gian-nah-tah and several of the other younger braves of the Be-don-ko-he. Chief Co-si-to was there with a band of his Chi-e-a-hen warriors; but there was disappointment in the voice of Na-chi-ta when he told that the other tribes had refused to join them.

Nan-ta-do-tash headed the izze-nantans who were preparing big medicine for use against the enemy, and with his own hands he prepared a phylactery for Shoz-Dijiji, calling down many blessings upon it.

The feast and the war dance aroused the braves to the highest pitch of excitement, to which the women added by their savage denunciation of the enemy and their demands upon their braves to go forth like men and slay the hated white-eyes; and when the dance was over the squaws accompanied the war party for several miles out of camp toward the point the chiefs had chosen for attack upon the morrow.

166

XIX

WHITE AND RED

IN a ranch house on the banks of the Gila, between Fort Thomas and the San Carlos Indian Agency, Wichita Billings awoke early on a beautiful, bright April morning.

She had ridden down from Thomas on the previous day with a Signal Corps detachment that was repairing the line of government telegraph, for a day's visit with the wife of the rancher. Tomorrow they would be back and she would return to the post with them.

Hearing her hostess already in the kitchen the girl dressed quickly and joined her. It was very early, yet already the rancher and his men were busy with the feeding and the chores. The daily life of the ranch had commenced, as it always did, in the cool of the morning, for one soon learns to take advantage of any respite from the intense heat of Arizona's middays.

Molly Pringe hummed a gay song as she fed sticks of cottonwood to the hungry range while Chita stirred the buckwheat batter. The odor of coffee and frying bacon was in the air. The women chatted as they worked. There was a great chirping of birds among the foliage of the two trees that shaded the front of the house.

Later in the day would come heat and silence. From behind the brow of a low ridge north of the ranch house a band of painted warriors surveyed the scene. They were Chi-e-a-hen and Tats-ah-das-ay-go, the Quick Killer, led them, for Tats-ah-das-ay-go was a war chief of the Chi-e-a-hen. With him today was Shoz-Dijiji, a war chief of the Be-don-ko-he; but Shoz-Dijiji rode as a warrior, since his tribe had refused to join the Chi-e-a-hen and Cho-kon-en upon the war trail. Just below them they saw a few white men moving about the corrals and sheds; they saw smoke pouring from the chimney of the ranch house—there the women would be.

Heber Pringe raised a forkful of hay to toss it over into the corral where several saddle ponies stood. As he did so he faced the ridge a few hundred yards away and instantly the fork stopped in mid-air, for at that moment a dozen savage warriors had urged their wiry mounts over the top and were already quirting them into a run down the hill.

"Apaches!" yelled Pringe and started for the house on a run.

Simultaneously, realizing that they had been seen, the warriors broke into the fierce Apache war whoop and, firing as they advanced, charged at a mad run down the hill in an effort to intercept the men before they reached the house, toward which all of them were now running amidst the shriek and whine of bullets, the yells of the savages spurring them on.

Pringe, who was in the lead, fell at the threshold of his home as a quartet of savages cut off the balance of the white men, who then turned toward the bunk house where they might make a better stand than in the open. With such swiftness had the hostiles struck that the women in the kitchen had scarcely more than grasped the significance of the attack when a burly brave shouldered into their presence. For an instant he stood in the doorway, his cruel face hideous with bands of green and blue and the red blood of a fresh killed rabbit. From behind him three other pairs of fierce eyes glared savagely across his shoulders out of faces streaked with war paint. Molly Pringe and Wichita Billings, trapped, unarmed, stood there helpless, momentarily frozen into inactivity by surprise and terror.

The older woman, standing before the stove, was the first to react to the menace of those sinister intruders. Seizing a hot frying pan filled with bubbling fat she hurled it at the head of the leading savage, at Tats-ah-das-ay-go, war chief of the Chi-e-a-hen. He fended the missile with a swart forearm, but much of the boiling contents spattered upon his naked body, eliciting a roar of rage and pain, spurring him to action.

Springing across the kitchen he seized Molly Pringe by the hair and forced her back upon the red-hot stove as he wielded his great butcher knife before the horrified eyes of Wichita Billings, then he turned upon her as, with clothing afire, the body of her friend slipped to the floor. Wichita Billings neither screamed nor fainted as death stared her in the face. In her heart she breathed a prayer, not for life, but for death quick and merciful, such as had been meted to Molly Pringe.

She saw the rage-distorted face of the Apache relax as his eyes fell upon her; she saw him pause in his advance; she saw the sudden change that marked a new thought in that demoniacal brain; she saw and shuddered. She would make him kill her! She raised the mixing bowl to hurl it in his face just as another warrior leaped into the room and seized the wrist of Tats-ah-das-ay-go. The girl stood with the bowl poised above her head, but she did not hurl it. Slowly her hands dropped before her as she recognized Shoz-Dijiji.

"Do not kill," said Shoz-Dijiji to Tats-ah-das-ay-go. "She is my friend."

168

"Who are you, Be-don-ko-he, to give orders to Tats-ah-das-ay-go, war chief of the Chi-e-a-hen?" demanded the other, wrenching his wrist from the grasp of Shoz-Dijiji.

"She is mine. I take her." He took a step forward toward the girl, and as he did so the Be-don-ko-he stepped between them and with a terrific shove sent Tats-ah-das-ay-go reeling across the room. Recovering himself, loud Apache curses upon his lips, the Chi-e-a-hen sprang for Shoz-Dijiji with up-raised knife; but the Be-don-ko-he was too quick, his Colt spoke from his hip and Tats-ah-das-ay-go crumpled to the floor of the kitchen beside the last victim of his ferocity.

"Come! Quick!" snapped Shoz-Dijiji, seizing the girl by the wrist; but there were two more Chi-e-a-hen in the doorway to dispute the ethics of his action with the Be-don-ko-he.

It is not difficult to foment strife between the members of different Apache tribes, and in this case there was little background of friendly intercourse to interpose its mediating influence between Shoz-Dijiji and these two warriors who had just seen him slay one of their great men; nor did Shoz-Dijiji expect anything other than opposition as he swung toward the doorway.

Nor was he waiting for opposition to develop. As he wheeled, he fired, and as one of the braves lurched forward upon his face the other turned and ran from the house. Behind him came Shoz-Dijiji, dragging Wichita Billings with him. In the yard stood many ponies, among them a pinto stallion and toward him the Be-don-ko-he ran swiftly, while the fleeing Chi-e-a-hen sped, shouting, in the direction of the warriors surrounding the bunk house.

Shoz-Dijiji leaped to the back of Nejeunee and leaning down offered a flexed arm to the girl. Grasping it, she sprang upward as Shoz-Dijiji straightened, lifting her, swinging her to the pony's rump behind him.

The Chi-e-a-hen had attracted the attention of some of his fellows and was leading them back at a run as Shoz-Dijiji reined Nejeunee toward the south and gave him his head with a whispered word in his pointed ear. Straight toward the Gila he rode, and as he reached the bank a backward glance revealed four Chi-e-a-hen braves quirting in pursuit. Down the steep bank into the muddy Gila slid Nejeunee, across the turgid stream he splashed, and up the bank beyond. Behind them came the yelling, avenging four. Out across level land toward the mountains sped the pinto stallion while a bewildered girl clung to the naked shoulders of the copper giant before her. His black hair, wind blown, tossed before her eyes; his bow and arrow-filled quiver touched her cheek; at his hip was the Colt that had won them escape, and in his right hand he waved a

169

cavalry carbine as he shouted defiance and insults at the Chi-e-a-hen trailing behind. Her rescue, if it was rescue, had occurred so unexpectedly and had developed with such swiftness, amid action fierce and bloody, that Wichita Billings had had no time to consider what it might portend. Was she being rescued, or had there merely been a change of captors? She wondered, now that she could find an instant in which to think at all. She had recognized Shoz-Dijiji the instant that he had interfered with her assailant. Unquestionably he had been one of the raiding party that had attacked the ranch, a hostile on the warpath. She knew how fierce and terrible they became under the spell of the weird rites of their medicine men, the savagely inciting oratory of their chiefs, the taunts and urgings of their squaws. She knew that these forces often transformed friendly, peaceable Indians into fiends of the most brutish ferocity; and slowly a new fear entered her heart, but even this was temporarily driven out a moment later as the Chi-e-a-hen warriors began firing at them. It is true that the bullets went wide, as a running pony makes a difficult seat for a marksman, but there was always the chance that a bullet might find them.

Over his shoulder Shoz-Dijiji spoke to her. "Take my six-shooter," he said, "and fire it at them. Mebbyso they no come so fast."

Wrenching the heavy weapon from its holster the girl turned about as far as she could and fired back at the leading pursuer. The bullet must have come close to him, for he reined in a little, increasing the distance between them. A moment later she fired again, and one of the Chi-e-a-hen threw up both hands and toppled from his pony. With renewed yells the remaining three opened fire more rapidly, but they kept a greater distance.

"I got one," she said to Shoz-Dijiji.

The brave little pinto, straining every nerve, fought courageously on under his double burden, but as the gradual ascent toward the mountains became a more pronounced upward gradient the pace told on him, and Shoz-Dijiji knew that though he might run until his brave heart burst he could not escape even inferior ponies that carried but a single rider.

Ahead was a low outcropping of uptilted sedimentary rock, and toward this the Be-don-ko-he reined his war pony while behind the three clung like pursuing wolves, occasionally firing a shot which was often returned by the girl. Through a gap in the rocky escarpment rode Shoz-Dijiji. He wheeled quickly to one side and brought Nejeunee to his haunches, at the same instant throwing a leg over the pony's withers, and as he touched the ground dragging Wichita down beside him.

"Lie down!" he commanded, pointing toward the natural breastwork, and then he turned toward Nejeunee and spoke an Apache word in his ear. Instantly the animal went down upon his knees and rolled over on his side; the three were effectually hidden from the fire of the enemy.

Throwing himself down beside the girl Shoz-Dijiji raised his carbine above the top of the ledge and took careful aim at the foremost of the Chi-e-a-hen. At the shot the fellow dropped. Again Shoz-Dijiji fired and the mount of another stumbled and fell. That was enough for the Chi-e-a-hen. Running toward his remaining companion, the warrior who had been dismounted leaped to a seat behind him and the two wheeled and scurried away while the bullets of the Be-don-ko-he whistled about their ears. For a while Shoz-Dijiji watched the retreating enemy in silence, or scanned the country closely in all directions. Presently he turned toward the girl.

"They come back," he said.

"What makes you think so?"

"I know. They come back with many braves. They want kill Shoz-Dijiji. They want you."

"When they are out of sight I can ride for the post," she suggested; but she wondered if he would let her, after all.

"No," he replied. "Apaches everywhere." He waved his hand broadly from west to east and back again. "Apaches on the war trail. You no reach post. Shoz-Dijiji no reach post, mebby. Shoz-Dijiji take you to his own people—to the Be-don-ko-he. You be safe there with Sons-ee-ah-ray and Geronimo."

To Shoz-Dijiji no promise could have seemed more reassuring, no name so fraught with assurance of protection than that of the kind old man who had always defended him, the powerful chief whose very name was a bulwark of safety for any friend. To Wichita Billings the suggestion awakened naught but fear and the name only horror. Geronimo! The fiend, the red devil, murderer, torturer, scourge of two nations! She trembled at the mere thought of him.

"No!" she cried. "Let me go back to the post, to my own people."

"You would never reach them. Tomorrow we can be with the Be-don-ko-he. They are not upon the war trail. When the fighting is over I will take you back to your people."

"I am afraid," she said.

"Afraid of what?"

"Afraid of Geronimo."

He looked at her in surprise. "You will be safe with him," he said. "Geronimo is my father."

She looked up at him aghast. God have mercy upon her—alone with the son of Geronimo!

"Come!" said Shoz-Dijiji. "Pretty soon they come back. No find us here. Mebbyso they follow. We go now they no catch. We stay, they catch, Come!"

He had mounted Nejeunee and was waiting for her. Tall and straight he sat his war pony. The war band about his brow confined his black hair; across his face, from ear to ear, spread a wide band of vermilion; a single necklace of silver and turquoise encircled his neck and lay upon his deep chest; beaded war moccasins encased his feet and legs.

From the painted face two steady eyes regarded her intently, searchingly, conveying the impression that they saw beneath the surface, deep into the secret recesses of her mind. They were not savage eyes now, not the eyes that she had seen flash upon Tats-ah-das-ay-go, but, rather, steadfast, friendly eyes that were, at the same time, commanding eyes. They waited, but there was no inquiry in them as to whether she would obey; that, they took for granted.

Still the girl hesitated. What was she to do? As deeply rooted within her as is man's natural repugnance for snakes was her fear and distrust of all Apaches, yet Shoz-Dijiji seemed different. Three times he had had her in his power and had offered her no harm; twice he had saved her from harm at the hands of others, this last time at the cost of the lives of four of his fellows, subjecting himself to what future dangers she could only too well conjecture, aware as she was of the Indian's penchant for vengeance. Had it been a matter only of trusting herself to him alone, perhaps she would not have hesitated; but there were the other members of his tribe—the squaws. She had heard stories of the cruelties of the squaws toward white women—and Geronimo! She recalled every hideous atrocity that had ever been laid at the door of this terrible old man, and she shrank from the thought of permitting herself to be taken to his hidden den and delivered into his cruel and, bloody hands. Shoz-Dijiji had ridden close to her side. "You come!" he said, and reaching down he swept her up into his arms and headed Nejeunee into the hills. Thus was the decision made for her.

He held her so easily, as though she had been a little child. He was so strong, and his voice so commanding, without harshness, that she felt almost reassured even with the coincident realization that she was being carried off by force.

"I know why you afraid," said Shoz-Dijiji presently. "You hear bad stories about Apaches. You hear much talk, bad talk; but always from mouth of enemies of Apache. You wait. You see how Apache treat friend. You no be afraid. You savvy?"

Wichita Billings had thought that she knew this part of Arizona rather well, but the Apache took her to a place, far back in what

172

seemed utterly arid mountains, that she had never dreamed of. It was a tiny, well-hidden canyon; but it boasted that most precious of treasures, water; and there were a few trees and a little grass for Nejeunee. The water seeped out from between rocks, wet the ground for a few feet from its source and disappeared again into the sand and gravel of a little wash; but after Shoz-Dijiji scooped out a hole with his hands it quickly filled and there was ample water for them all, even thirsty Nejeunee, though it was a long time before he got his fill.

After they had drunk Shoz-Dijiji hobbled Nejeunee, lest he stray too far, then he removed his cartridge belt and revolver and laid them beside the girl, together with his carbine. "You stay here," he said. "Mebbyso Shoz-Dijiji catchem rabbit. Go see," and unslinging his bow he walked away. He went up the little canyon and soon disappeared.

Wichita Billings glanced down at the weapons beside her and up at the hobbled pony grazing a few yards from her. How easy it would be, she thought. She gathered up the cartridge belt with the holster and revolver attached and rose to her feet. How easily she could outdistance pursuit upon that swift pony. It seemed strange that the Apache should have left her alone with his weapons and his pony; he might have known that she could escape. She wondered why he had done it and then the answer came to her—he trusted her.

She stood there for several minutes with the belt dangling in her hand. He trusted her! And what return was she about to make his confidence and his sacrifices? Did he deserve this at her hands— to be left afoot and primitively armed in a country swarming with enemy soldiers and equally hostile Indians?

Wichita let the cartridge belt slip from her fingers to the ground and sat down again to wait, her mind relieved with the acceptance of a definite determination to put her trust implicitly in the honor of Shoz-Dijiji. She tried to remember only his generous acts, his friendly attitude, his noble mien, and the great strength and courage that proclaimed him a safe refuge and a natural protector. She wanted to forget that he was a renegade, a savage Cheeracow Apache. And then he returned, as silently as he had departed; and she saw his almost naked body and the war paint on his face, and it took all the courage of her brave little heart to smile up at him in greeting as he stopped before her, tall, straight, magnificent, and laid a rabbit and brace of quail at her feet.

Then it was that Shoz-Dijiji did something the significance of which passed above the head of the white girl, something that would have told her more plainly than words the unique position that she held in the regard of the red man. There, with a woman present, the Apache warrior prepared the game, built the fire and cooked the meal. Wichita Billings took it as a matter of course. Shoz-Dijiji excused it, mentally, upon the ground that women were helpless fools, that one of them would not know how to build a fire without matches and with very little fuel, how to prepare properly the quail and the rabbit.

It was almost dusk when they had finished their frugal meal. There were no dishes to wash, but Shoz-Dijiji carefully buried all signs of their fire and the remnants of their repast. By dark they were moving south again upon the back of the rested Nejeunee. Down the mountains, out onto a plain they rode, and by midnight entered another range farther south. Here Shoz-Dijiji halted again, built a rude shelter for Wichita and told her to sleep, while he threw himself down upon the ground a few yards away. All the following day they rode, through a rough, trailless, mountain country, the brave finding food where there was none to be seen and water where the girl would have sworn no water could exist.

Wichita was tired almost to exhaustion, yet the man seemed not to notice that they had been undergoing any hardships whatsoever. To her he seemed a man of iron, and almost as silent; and as the hours passed slowly, monotonously, painfully, there grew within her a sense of trustfulness, of security that she could imagine harboring for no other man she had ever known. He seemed a very well of resourcefulness; a sanctuary as granitic, as eternal as the everlasting bed rock they sometimes crossed—a demi-god moving surely through a world of his own creation where there were no secrets that might be hid from his omniscience.

And thus at last they came to the camp of the Be-don-ko-he, but Wichita Billings was no longer afraid; where Shoz-Dijiji was, there was safety. As they rode into the camp, there was a tendency to crowd about them and there were looks in the eyes of some of the squaws that would have filled her with apprehension had not the great shoulders of Shoz-Dijiji loomed so reassuringly close; but after he had spoken to them, in words she could not understand, their attitude changed. Scowling squaws smiled up at her and one or two stroked her skirt in a friendly way, for Shoz-Dijiji had told them that she was his friend—a friend of all the Be-don-ko-he.

They dismounted before a rude tepee where squatted a wrinkled man and two women. "This is Geronimo, my father," said Shoz-Dijiji.

The girl looked, almost fearfully, into the face of the old archdemon. She saw stern features there, and a wide mouth with almost bloodless lips, and blue eyes, so uncharacteristic of the

Apache. Contorted with rage, she could sense that it might be a face of utter cruelty; but today, as he listened to the words of his son, it was just the face of a benevolent, tired, old man.

"Shoz-Dijiji brings a captive from the war trail?" Geronimo had asked when the two first stood before him.

"No," replied Shoz-Dijiji, "a friend."

"Shoz-Dijiji has taken a white-eyed one for his woman?" demanded the old chief.

Again the younger man shook his head. "She was a friend to Shoz-Dijiji," he explained. "She gave him food and water and a pony when the soldiers of the pindah lickoyee were hunting him.

"When Shoz-Dijiji was upon the war trail with the Chi-e-a-hen they were about to kill her. They would not stop when Shoz-Dijiji asked them to. Shoz-Dijiji killed the Chi-e-a-hen, and because the country was filled with Apaches upon the war trail and Shoz-Dijiji knew that many soldiers would come, he brought her here to his own people, where she will be safe until the trouble is over; then he will return her to her people."

Geronimo turned his eyes upon Wichita. "Ink-tah," he said.

"Geronimo says, 'sit down,'" translated Shoz-Dijiji and the girl did as she was bid. Geronimo patted her hand and smiled.

"You will be safe with the Be-don-ko-he," he said. "We are your friends."

When Shoz-Dijiji had repeated the words in English, Wichita knew that they were true, yet at the same time it seemed beyond belief that she could be sitting at the side of the notorious Geronimo in the remote fastness of his hidden camp and yet be as innocent of fear as though safe within the protecting walls of her father's ranch house. The thought came to her that perhaps she was safer here, since at least she was not menaced by the threat of hostile Apaches.

That night she slept in the tepee of the mother-in-law of Geronimo and as she dozed off to sleep she smiled as she thought of the terrors that that name had always conjured to her mind and of the surprise and incredibility that were certain to mark the reception of her story by her father and her friends when she was restored to them—sleeping in the tepee of the mother-in-law of Geronimo, not twenty paces from the war chief of all the Apaches.

175

XX

COME BACK!

THROUGH that strange medium for the dissemination of information that is one of the remarkable phenomena of the life of primitive peoples, word of the activities of the hostiles was carried to the stronghold of Geronimo.

The Be-don-ko-he knew of the attack upon San Carlos Agency which resulted in the killing of Sterling, chief of Indian Scouts, and several other whites; knew that Chief Loco, successor to the dead Victorio, had joined the hostiles with all his Chi-hen-ne, men, women and children, and that the whole band was heading south toward Mexico.

They had news of the fight in Horse Shoe Canyon, and learned of the killing of Yuma Bill and three Yuma scouts and three soldiers in that fight; followed the flight of the hostiles along the rough crest of Stein's Peak Range, down into the San Simon Valley, and from there into the Chiricahua Mountains; knew that they had scattered there, only to meet at another point; saw them safely all the way through Whitewater Canyon, across the mountains, down Animas Valley toward Guadalupe Pass, and near there across into Mexico.

Shoz-Dijiji kept Wichita posted on all that transpired, but he would not start back with her toward her home until he was sure that the last of the hostiles was out of the country, for they had scattered twice and he was not sure that all had crossed the border. Too, there was the danger from the troops, but that was secondary because it menaced only himself. She tried to tell him that he would be safe from the soldiers as long as he was with her, for when she had told them that he had rescued her from the hostiles they would not only be friendly but would reward him, but he shook his head.

"They kill Shoz-Dijiji first; ask you about him after," he said.

They were sitting beneath the shade of a tree upon the shoulder of the mountain, over-looking the camp of the Be-don-ko-he. In the distance they could see the wide plain stretching to other mountains.

The girl had noticed that Shoz-Dijiji always seemed to be where he could see to a great distance when he rested or rather idled, for he never seemed to be in the need of rest. Sometimes he scanned

176

the horizon through a pair of field glasses. Finally he touched the glasses to call her attention to them.

"You know who belong these?" he asked.

She shook her head.

"Your lover," he said, laughing.

"My lover!" she exclaimed. "What do you mean? I have no lover."

He looked at her intently for a moment. "You no love King?" he asked.

It was her turn to laugh. "He is only a friend," she said. "Are those his glasses?"

"You no love him?" he insisted.

"Of course not."

"Shoz-Dijiji know that, he kill him that time," he said, quite simply.

Impulsively she laid a hand upon his arm. "Oh, Shoz-Dijiji," she cried, "why do you want to kill everyone? You are such a good man. Why don't you put away your weapons and come in to the reservation?"

"Shoz-Dijiji does not want to kill everyone," replied the brave. "Shoz-Dijiji does not want to kill you. If Shoz-Dijiji put away his weapons, no hunt, no fight; what for he live? Be reservation Indian?" There was a wealth of unveiled contempt in his voice. "Let agent cheat him, starve him? Let white man laugh at him, make fun of him? No!"

"But they would help you, Shoz-Dijiji. I would help you."

"Yes, you would help me; but you would always feel sorry for me because I am an Indian. I do not want the help of the white-eyes. I do not think that they would help me. Have they ever helped the Indian? What can they give the Indian that Usen has not already given him? Only, they take away what Usen has given.

"What has the pindah lickoyee better than the Shis-Inday? Is he braver? Is he more honest? Can he teach the Indian how and where to find food and clothing? No, the pindah lickoyee would starve where the Indian grows fat. He would go naked where the Indian finds more clothing than he needs. Has he more sense? He has none. See what he has done to this country.

"Before he came there was plenty for all, but like a fool he set out to kill every living thing that Usen had put here. He robs the Indian of his food, but also he robs himself of food—food that cost only a little effort to obtain—food that, hunted as the Indian knows how to hunt, always increased in numbers.

"What has he done for us? He is trying to take away from us the ways of our fathers—our dances, our medicine men, everything that

177

we hold sacred; and in return he gives us whiskey and shoots us wherever he finds us. I do not think the pindah lickoyee are such good men that they can tell the Indian how to be good.

"Around every post and agency the white men are always trying to ravish our women. The women of the Apache are good women. When they are not we cut off their noses. How many Apache women have you ever seen whose noses had been cut off? Do you think we want to come and live beside such men? Do you think there is anything that they can teach us that is better than our fathers taught us?

"You think it is bad to kill. Yes, it is bad to kill; but it is better to kill like men and braves, openly and upon the war trail, than to kill by lies. Our people are told great lies to get them to come into the reservations, and there they are starved; and if they leave the reservation to hunt for food for their women and children, without a pass from the agent who is robbing them, then the soldiers come and shoot them. No, Shoz-Dijiji never be reservation Indian!"

"I am sorry," she said. "I never thought of it from your side. I can see that in some ways you are right; but in others you are wrong. All white men are not bad."

"All Indians are not bad," he replied quickly, "but the pindah lickoyee treat them all alike—bad."

For some time they sat in silence, the Apache watching the girl's face, his own expressionless.

What was passing behind that granitic mask? Once he extended a hand toward her as though to touch her, then he drew it back quickly and sprang to his feet.

"Come!" he said, almost roughly. "We go back to camp."

Two days later Geronimo and Shoz-Dijiji thought that it would be safe to return Wichita to her home, and the young war chief and the girl set out upon the long journey, which was but a repetition of that which had ended at the camp of the Be-don-ko-he.

During the journey Wichita could not but notice that the brave scarcely let his eyes leave her face, a thing of which she had had a growing consciousness for at least two days before they left the camp. Had she not come to trust him so implicitly she would have found it difficult not to have acknowledged something of nervous apprehension as she felt his gaze constantly upon her; but he took no other liberties with her—just looked at her through those steady, inscrutable eyes.

Every journey must have an end and at last the two stood upon the very hill above her father's ranch where they had stood upon another occasion. Shoz-Dijiji drew rein and dismounted. "I will wait here until you are safe in the house of your father," he said.

"You are not coming down with me?" she exclaimed, surprised.
"No."

"I want you to, Shoz-Dijiji. I want my father to know you, and thank you for what you have done for me," she insisted.

"Me no go," he replied. The girl became suddenly conscious of a feeling almost of panic. Was she never to see Shoz-Dijiji again, this good friend, this best of friends? She realized, and the realization came as a distinct shock, that this man of another race had suddenly filled a great emptiness in her life—an emptiness the existence of which she had never before realized—and that life was going to be very different without him. Already she felt a great loneliness creeping over her.

She was standing beside him and now, she turned and came close, putting her two palms upon his breast. "Please, Shoz-Dijiji," she begged. "Please come down—I do not want you to go away."

The contact of her hands upon him broke the iron will of the Apache. The habitual mask behind which he hid his emotions dropped away—it was a new Shoz-Dijiji into whose face the girl looked. He seized her in his arms and pressed her close; his lips covering hers.

She struck at his great chest and sought to push him away; she held her head from him and he saw the horror in her eyes. Then it was that he released her.

"Shoz-Dijiji sorry," he said. "For days he fight the great fire burning in his brain, burning up his heart. Shoz-Dijiji thought he was strong; he did not know how much stronger is love—until you touched him. But you are right. You are white—Shoz-Dijiji is Apache. White girl could not love Apache. That is right." He vaulted to the back of Nejeunee. "Shoz-Dijiji sorry. Good-bye!"

She watched him ride away and the panic and the loneliness gripped her like fingers of flesh and blood that sought to choke life and love and happiness from her. She saw him disappear beyond a hill to the south and she took a step after him, her hands outstretched in dumb pleading for his return that her lips had not the courage to voice aloud. She stood thus for a minute and then her arms dropped limply to her side and she turned back toward her father's house.

A few steps she took and then she wheeled suddenly about and extended her arms again, in supplication.

"Shoz-Dijiji!" she cried, "Shoz-Dijiji, come back!"

But Shoz-Dijiji, war chief of the Be-don-ko-he, did not hear.

THE END

Milton Keynes UK
Ingram Content Group UK Ltd.
UKHW042137170823
427025UK00003B/12/J